Photo by J. K. St. Joseph.

LULWORTH COVE.
Aerial view from the South-east.

Photo by E. R. Martin.

STAIR HOLE AND LULWORTH COVE.
With Gad Cliff, Hounstout and St. Alban's Head
in the distance.

THE
DORSET COAST

A Geological Guide

BY

G. M. DAVIES

SECOND EDITION
WITH 14 PHOTOGRAPHS
AND 33 FIGURES

LONDON
ADAM AND CHARLES BLACK

FIRST PUBLISHED 1935
BY THOMAS MURBY AND CO

SECOND EDITION 1956
REPRINTED 1964
A. AND C. BLACK LTD
4, 5 AND 6 SOHO SQUARE LONDON W.1

MADE IN GREAT BRITAIN
PRINTED BY JOHN DICKENS AND CO LTD
NORTHAMPTON

PREFACE TO THE FIRST EDITION

The experience of many years has provéd the Dorset coast to be an ideal training ground for field parties of geological students. There the beginner sees folds and faults as clearly recognisable as in text-book diagrams, while the advanced student finds many problems still inviting investigation. The fossil-collector can make large bags, and the geographer, seeing how clearly surface features mirror the underlying structure, is more than ever convinced that geology is the foundation of geography.

It is primarily for such students that this book has been written. It may supplement and crystallise the field teaching for those who go in conducted parties; and it enables the lone hunter to find his quarry without having to refer to the scattered literature on the subject.

But there is another class of reader who may find this guide-book useful—the man who has never taken a course of lectures in geology and may have no idea of making a study of it, but whose interest is aroused by the fossils or by the scenery of the Dorset coast. As a holiday pastime, field geology has much to recommend it. Laying aside popular detective fiction, one may become a detective for the time, collecting and interpreting clues buried in the rocks. The pursuit may even be found to rival in interest such respectable occupations as golf and bridge.

Help has been received from many friends, and I must particularly thank my colleagues Dr. L. F. Spath, whose intimate knowledge of the Mesozoic rocks and their fossils has been generously put at my disposal, and Dr. F. Smithson, who has re-drawn all the figures that appear in the text. The

cliff diagrams have been prepared from the six-inch maps **and**
embody geological details from the work of Strahan, Rowe,
Lang and Arkell. A tribute must also be paid to the use made
of that great storehouse of facts, " The Jurassic System in
Great Britain," by Dr. W. J. Arkell.

G. M. D.

Birkbeck College
  (University of London).

April, 1935.

CONTENTS

ILLUSTRATIONS IN THE TEXT

PLATES

THE DORSET COAST

I.—INTRODUCTION

Dorset is not so famed for the beauty of its coast line as its neighbour, Devon : hence it is not so over-run with visitors. Nor has it the nearness to London that is turning the Sussex coast into one long street. Bournemouth spreads its huge bulk across the eastern boundary, but Bournemouth and Studland are separated by more than a few miles of road. Dorset is still unspoiled, and it will be an evil day when Poole Harbour is bridged and when the twisty lanes that lead to Tyneham and Kimmeridge are made more attractive to motorists. Only Lulworth and, latterly, Portland Bill attract the crowd. Even the towns—Lyme Regis, Bridport, Weymouth, Swanage—all have long-established industries of their own and are not primarily visitor-traps.

Yet the county has scenery of no small merit. Golden Cap, Durdle Door, Worbarrow Bay, Ballard Down, all are as delightful as their names, and linger in the memory with more famous spots. Many a lovely old manor-house, or church in harmony with its surroundings, adds to the natural beauty. Some have been described by the architect-novelist-poet of Wessex, and Hardy's descriptions will be appreciated the more after seeing the originals of Wellbridge and Oxley Hall, as well as the more nebulous Egdon Heath.

To the student of geology Dorset is well known, at least from books. Kimmeridge Clay, Portland and Purbeck Beds, familiar in our mouths as household words, all have their type-localities in the county, while Charmouth lends its name to a division of the Lower Lias. But book-reading is a poor substitute for hammering the actual rocks and seeing how they fit into the structural fabric of the country. The whole range of the Jurassic rocks is seen in the Dorset cliffs; most of them yield plenty of fossils, and there are few areas where a beginner can get so clear an insight into geological structures and the work of the agents of erosion.

This guide-book is intended to help the student to make the best use of his time in Dorset, without preliminary work in the library. It tells him what is to be seen in each section of the coast. The descriptions are necessarily brief, but the references to Dorset literature at the end will aid further work on points that arouse interest. The cliff sections illustrate the lie of the rocks on the actual coast; for the inland outcrops the colour-printed one-inch maps of the Geological Survey are available. Manuscript copies of the six-inch maps, coloured geologically, may be consulted, if required, at the Geological Museum at South Kensington, where, too, geological models and series of characteristic Dorset fossils may be seen.

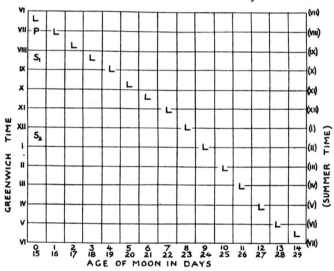

FIG. 1. TIDES ON THE DORSET COAST.
Average time of high water at Lyme Regis (L), Portland (P) and Swanage (S₁ and S₂), according to the age of the moon.

The book is divided into three sections, dealing with west, central, and east Dorset, Bridport (or Lyme Regis), Weymouth and Swanage forming convenient centres. Each section begins with a general account of the geology, followed by a detailed description of the coast, from west to east.

The Dorset cliffs are fairly accessible, with the exception of the precipitous cliffs of Portland Stone and Chalk and those in the Kimmeridge district. The clays and shales often give rise to terraced cliffs, due to hard bands forming shelves or undercliffs. Landslips too form shelves tilted gently inland and backed by slopes that may be nearly vertical at the top.

These shelves are accessible at some points, if not all. They often hold up water, and after a wet winter they may form lakes of mud from which mud-glaciers creep down the gullies. It is easy to sink knee-deep in these.

Care should be exercised when walking beneath cliffs that show signs of falling. The cliffs of Liassic shale in the western part of the coastline give a rain of small jagged fragments which, descending from some height and acquiring a rapid spin, are more dangerous missiles than they appear to be.

Outstanding cliffs of Chalk or Portland Stone descend into fairly deep water; even at low tide there is no shore exposed beneath them. The Kimmeridgian and Corallian cliffs may be washed by the waves at high water. Elsewhere, the high tide may restrict walking to a very rough zone beneath the cliffs. The state of the tide should therefore always be ascertained before planning one's programme.

High water at Lyme Regis and Bridport occurs about $4\frac{1}{2}$ hours later than at London Bridge, and the time of high water at London Bridge can be found in the daily paper or in Whitaker's Almanac. *Fig.* 1 gives a general idea of the time of high water at Lyme Regis according to the age of the moon.

At Portland, Swanage and Poole the tides are complicated by a second tidal wave, and the variations are too great for an average figure to have any value, except at new moon and full moon; nor can the times of high water there be ascertained by reference to such simple tides as those at London Bridge. Information as to these tides should be sought from local sources. Portland has two low waters each tide, while from Swanage eastward to Southampton two high waters occur.

This second tidal wave is often said to have travelled round Great Britain and through the Straits of Dover. It may with more reason be ascribed to a wave reflected from the northward-trending coast of France between the mouth of the Somme and Cape Gris Nez.

II.—WESTERN SECTION

The rocks of the Dorset coast are mainly those of the Jurassic System, the outcrop of which stretches northward to the coast of Yorkshire. The Lower Jurassic (or Liassic) rocks are seen in West Dorset, dipping eastward beneath younger beds, while the Upper Jurassics are exposed in Mid and East Dorset.

The desert conditions of the Permian and Triassic Periods, under which the red rocks of the Devon cliffs were formed,

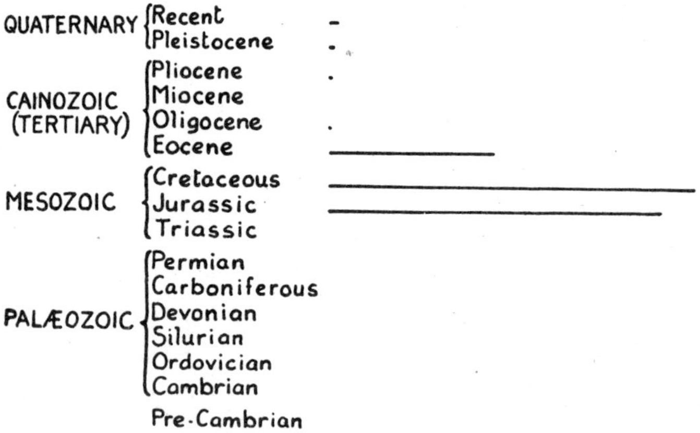

QUATERNARY	Recent	-
	Pleistocene	.
CAINOZOIC (TERTIARY)	Pliocene	.
	Miocene	
	Oligocene	.
	Eocene	————————
MESOZOIC	Cretaceous	—————————————
	Jurassic	—————————————
	Triassic	
PALÆOZOIC	Permian	
	Carboniferous	
	Devonian	
	Silurian	
	Ordovician	
	Cambrian	
	Pre-Cambrian	

FIG. 2. THE GEOLOGICAL SYSTEMS
with the relative areas of their outcrops in Dorset.

gave place to the shallow, land-locked and not quite normal Rhætic sea at the close of the Triassic. In Jurassic times, shelf-seas of moderate depth spread over a large part of England. The position of the coast line varied, as did the depth of the sea, but Brittany, Cornwall, Wales and most of Ireland seem to have formed part of a great North Atlantic continent, while another land-mass stretched eastward from the site of the London Basin into Belgium. There were islands in the Liassic sea in the neighbourhood of Cardiff and the Mendips. The land was of low relief, but no longer a desert, and its rivers discharged quantities of mud into the sea. Hence the Jurassic rocks are mainly clays and shales, with occasional

4

sands, limestones and ironstones, which were formed in shallower water. At times part of the sea-floor was raised to within reach of wave action and suffered erosion instead of continuous deposition. This caused a local break, or non-sequence, in the geological record.

The sea that covered the British area in Jurassic times was no land-locked basin. It communicated with the ocean, and newly-evolved forms of life entered it freely. It is by the fossil remains of these organisms that we are able to date the rocks and correlate those of the same age in different areas, even if they are of different lithological types. Geographical factors affected the distribution of faunas then as now, and forms that abounded in a sandy bay might not occur on the muddy bottom farther off shore, but after allowing for differences of facies there are still enough common elements in the fauna to allow of correlation. Thus it has been possible by means of fossils to establish a chronological division of sedimentary rocks side by side with lithological divisions such as the Bridport Sand and the Inferior Oolite.

As long ago as 1856 Oppel established certain broad divisions, or zones, for the Jurassic rocks. Each zone was based on an assemblage of fossils and named after one characteristic species; but the presence of that species is not essential to the recognition of the zone. These zones hold good, occurring everywhere in the same order, from Germany and the Juras to Scotland and Dorset.

Attempts at more refined chronological divisions have proved less reliable. In 1893 S. S. Buckman introduced the term *hemera* (=day) for the smallest unit of geological time, characterised by the acme of development of a species. Certain ammonites, in particular, abound in a few feet, or inches, of strata, and are rare or absent in rocks above and below. The deposits, formed during the hemera of a species, are sometimes called its epibole. Eventually Buckman built up a large series of hemeræ as sub-divisions of the Jurassic Period, and grouped them into biological Ages and Epochs. The local absence of an index species has been taken as evidence that during its hemera no deposition took place in the locality, or that penecontemporaneous erosion removed what had been deposited. Many non-sequences have been claimed on such grounds alone. Confirmatory evidence is always desirable, for the absence of a single species may be due to other causes. Even widely-distributed forms like the ammonites were not equally abundant everywhere at the same time, and the acme of a species is a more local event than was at first recognised.

TABLE OF STRATA IN SOUTH-WEST DORSET

			ZONES
	RECENT AND PLEISTOCENE	Shingle, Blown Sand, Alluvium, Valley Gravel, Clay-with-flints and angular flint and chert gravel (Unconformity)	
CRETACEOUS	SENONIAN	Upper Chalk feet 300	
	TURONIAN	Middle Chalk 100	
	CENOMANIAN	Lower Chalk 50	
	ALBIAN	Upper Greensand and Gault 150 (Unconformity)	
UPR. JURASSIC	CALLOVIAN	Kellaways Clay 50	*Proplanulites kœnigi*
		Upper Cornbrash ⎱ Lower Cornbrash ⎰ 30	*Macrocephalites macrocephalus* *Clydoniceras discus*
MIDDLE JURASSIC	BATHONIAN	Forest Marble 80	
		Fuller's Earth 150	*Oppelia fusca*
	BAJOCIAN	Inferior Oolite 20	*Parkinsonia parkinsoni* *Stephanoceras humphriesianum* *Otoites sauzei* *Sonninia sowerbyi* *Ludwigella concava* *Ludwigia murchisonæ*
		Bridport Sands 200	*Leioceras opalinum* (including *scissum*)
UPPER LIAS	TOARCIAN	Down Cliff Clay 70	*Lytoceras jurense*
		Junction Bed 3	*Hildoceras bifrons* *Harpoceras falciferum* *Dactylioceras tenuicostatum*
MIDDLE LIAS	DOMERIAN		*Paltopleuroceras spinatum*
		Thorncombe Sands 75 Down Cliff Sands 70 Eype Clay 190	*Amaltheus margaritatus*
LOWER LIAS	CHARMOUTHIAN	Green Ammonite Beds 100	*Prodactylioceras davœi*
		Belemnite Marls 80	*Tragophylloceras ibex* *Uptonia jamesoni*
	SINEMURIAN	Black Ven Marls 190	*Echioceras raricostatum* *Oxynoticeras oxynotum* *Asteroceras obtusum*
	HETTANGIAN	Blue Lias 100	*Arnioceras semicostatum* *Coroniceras bucklandi* *Schlotheimia angulata* *Psiloceras planorbis* *Ostrea* Beds
TRIAS	RHÆTIC	White Lias 25	
		Black Shales 20	*Avicula contorta*
	KEUPER	Keuper Marls 1,300	

As Spath pointed out in 1931, in the Juras many of Buckman's index species reach their acme in a different order, while sporadic occurrences extend their range over a much wider interval.

The strata seen in the coastal region of West Dorset are listed on page 6, while *Fig.* 3* shows the relative thicknesses of the Jurassic rocks. Their attitude as seen in the cliffs is shown in *Fig.* 6. Sheets 326 and 327 of the Geological Survey maps, New Series, one inch to a mile, show their outcrops.

The Keuper Marls, Black Shales of the Rhætic, and White Lias actually crop out beyond the county boundary. But the easterly dip carries them underground into Dorset, and a boring in search of coal west of Colway Manor House, on the left bank of the Lym, gave results which may be summarised as follows:—

		ft.	in.
DRIFT.	Soil, gravel and flints	10	8
LIAS.	Blue Lias	62	4
	White Lias	28	3
RHÆTIC.	Black Shales with *Avicula contorta,* etc.	32	5
KEUPER.	Red and green marls with gypsum ...	1,168	4
		1,302	0

Here the red and green marls with gypsum were clearly the products of the Triassic desert. The Black Shales yielded four characteristic Rhætic species of marine lamellibranchs, and indicate a marine transgression. As the Rhætic Beds in this country differ so markedly from the Trias, and are conformable with the Lias, it is convenient to include them with the latter in the Jurassic System. This is perhaps too parochial a view, and German geologists, familiar with the marine Trias and its fauna, regard the Rhætic as the top of the Trias, with better reason.

The **White Lias** seen in Pinhay Bay is generally included with the Rhætic. It yields, however, none of the characteristic Rhætic fossils, and in the absence of any representative of the Cotham Stone (or Landscape Marble) there is no reason for separating it from the Lias. It consists of thin bands of white limestone and yields small lamellibranchs such

---

* By colouring the sections in this book, using a distinctive colour for each bed, the student will learn a good deal of geology as well as making the sections clearer. The books of transparent water colours sold by photographic dealers are recommended for this purpose.

as *Ostrea liassica* and *Protocardia*. It was formerly exposed at Uplyme, but the quarries there are no longer worked.

The **Blue Lias** consists of alternations of clay-limestones with shale or clay, well seen in the cliffs and foreshore on both sides of Lyme Regis. The markedly banded appearance (layers, liers, Lias) is not due to deposition of two types of sediment alternately. The calcareous matter was at first disseminated fairly uniformly through the clay, but at a later stage it segregated to form nodules along certain bedding planes. Rhythmic precipitation, as described by Liesegang, may account for their position. The nodules grew larger and coalesced to form bands of limestone, some of which still have a very irregular surface. The shales owe their blue-grey colour to finely divided iron-pyrites.] The lower beds contain few fossils beyond *Ostrea liassica, Modiola minima,* and other lamellibranchs. Then come beds with the first of the zonal ammonites, *Psiloceras planorbis,* a smooth-shelled form usually found flattened in the shales. Some of the higher limestones, exposed in the reefs, are crowded with ammonites, including large examples of *Coroniceras bucklandi. Lima gigantea, Gryphæa arcuata* and *Pentacrinus* are abundant in places. The long brown bones of reptiles, especially *Ichthyosaurus,* are often exposed, and fish remains also occur.

Above the Blue Lias come the **Black Ven Marls,** a more purely argillaceous deposit although bands of fibrous calcite, or " beef," have given rise to the name **"Shales-with-Beef"** for the lower part. Limestone bands, either nodular or lenticular, break the series of shales. Some are crowded with ammonites, such as *Microderoceras birchi* just above the Shales-with-Beef, *Promicroceras planicosta* at the horizon of the Ammonite Marble of Marston Magna, and *Asteroceras stellare.*

The succeeding **Belemnite Marls,** light-grey in colour, contrast with the Black Ven Marls, or Black Marls, as they are often called. Belemnites abound in the marl and in the thin limestone band at the top, the Belemnite Stone.

The **Green Ammonite Beds** are a further series of clays containing various ammonites, *Androgynoceras latæcosta,* with its chambers filled with green calcite, being responsible for the name. This brings us to the top of the Lower Lias, a series of nearly 500 feet of clays with some limestone in the lower part. It has been. divided into three Stages : the Hettangian below*, the Sinemurian†, and the Charmouthian.

---

* From Hettange, in Lorraine, where it is well developed.
† From Sémur, Côte d'Or.

PLATE II.

A.   CHURCH CLIFFS, LYME REGIS.
Limestones and shales of the Blue Lias.

B.   WEAR CLIFF, BELOW GOLDEN CAP.
Showing the Three Tiers at the base of the Middle Lias, with the Green
Ammonite Beds below.

PLATE III.

A.   BURTON CLIFF, WITH EAST CLIFF IN THE DISTANCE.
Bridport Sands, with blocks of Inferior Oolite fallen from the top of
the cliff.

B.   FAULT IN WEST CLIFF, BRIDPORT.
Fuller's Earth on the left faulted down against
yellow Bridport Sands on the right.

The Middle Lias, or Domerian*, is more sandy. It begins with three bands of micaceous sandstone, the **Three Tiers,** which are conspicuous in the cliffs between Charmouth and Seatown. They occur at the base of the blue-grey, micaceous **Eype Clay,** which yields the zonal ammonite *Amaltheus margaritatus* and is capped by another micaceous sandstone, known as the **Starfish Bed** from the occurrence of the brittle-stars *Ophioderma egertoni* and *O. tenuibrachiata.*

Then follow the grey, laminated and micaceous **Down Cliff Sands** and the yellow micaceous **Thorncombe Sands,** and the top of the Middle Lias is represented by a few inches of ferruginous **Marlstone** at the base of the Junction Bed.

The **Junction Bed** of Down Cliff is a band of limestone, about three feet thick, at the junction of the Middle and Upper Lias. While the sands of the Middle Lias indicate rather shallower water than the clays of the Lower Lias, the Junction Bed represents a prolonged period of shallow, possibly lagoonal conditions, alternating with uplift and erosion. No clay or sand reached this locality. Much of the limestone is a fine-grained white lithographic stone, and the ammonites range from the Domerian *Paltopleuroceras spinatum* in the basal Marlstone layer through the greater part of the Toarcian†, or Upper Lias. They span a period during which fully three hundred feet of normal deposits were accumulating in Yorkshire. Deposition here was slow and discontinuous, breaks being indicated not only by the absence of certain species but by planes of erosion that bevel the fossils, whose matrix must already have been a hard stone at the time. Yet the succeeding deposit is joined to it compactly, and the Junction Bed forms a single bed of stone. Its top is another plane of erosion.

Above it come the grey **Down Cliff Clay** and the yellow **Bridport Sands,** which extend up into the Bajocian. The Upper Lias comprises the single Stage of the Toarcian, but Buckman subdivided it into the Whitbian below and the Yeovilian above.

The Bridport Sands pass up through sandy limestones into the **Inferior Oolite,** a limestone with scattered oolitic grains, some of which are ferruginous (iron-shot oolite). It is another highly-condensed sequence, slow deposition alternating with erosion, and the thickness of eleven feet on the Dorset coast represents nearly three hundred feet of limestone

---

* From Monte Domero, in Northern Italy.
† From Thouars, Deux-Sèvres.

DRAW

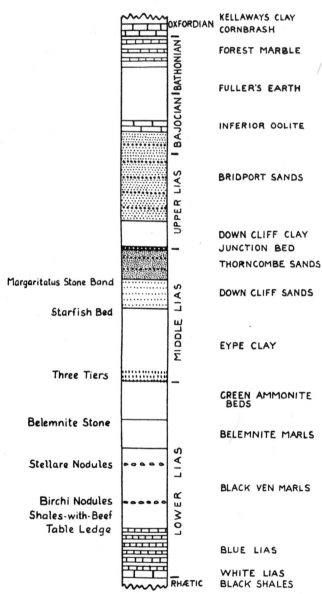

	OXFORDIAN	KELLAWAYS CLAY	
		CORNBRASH	
	BATHONIAN	FOREST MARBLE	
		FULLER'S EARTH	
	BAJOCIAN	INFERIOR OOLITE	
	UPPER LIAS	BRIDPORT SANDS	
		DOWN CLIFF CLAY	
		JUNCTION BED	
		THORNCOMBE SANDS	
Margaritatus Stone Band	MIDDLE LIAS	DOWN CLIFF SANDS	
Starfish Bed		EYPE CLAY	
Three Tiers		GREEN AMMONITE BEDS	
Belemnite Stone		BELEMNITE MARLS	
Stellare Nodules	LOWER LIAS	BLACK VEN MARLS	
Birchi Nodules			
Shales-with-Beef			
Table Ledge		BLUE LIAS	
	RHÆTIC	WHITE LIAS	
		BLACK SHALES	

FIG. 3. THE JURASSIC ROCKS OF SOUTH-WEST DORSET.
Scale: 1 inch to 250 feet.

in the Cotteswolds. The upper part of the Bridport Sands and the Inferior Oolite are included in the Bajocian* Stage, which may be subdivided into the Aalenian† below and the Vesulian ‡ above.

Another series of clays follows, known as the **Fuller's Earth** because their equivalent in the Bath district includes fuller's earth of economic value. A few inches of indurated marl at the base, the Scroff, yields *Oppelia fusca,* but ammonites are very scarce throughout the Bathonian Stage and brachiopods have been used as zonal indicators in their absence.

The Fuller's Earth passes up into the shelly limestones and clays of the **Forest Marble,** which takes its name from Wychwood Forest in Oxfordshire. This is the highest Jurassic rock exposed in the cliffs of West Dorset. No exposures of Cornbrash are seen in this part of the county, but at the Bridport Brick and Tile Works, near Bothenhampton, there is a splendid section in the Kellaways Clay.

Almost the whole of the Upper Jurassic and Lower Cretaceous is missing, and the **Gault** is the next deposit. While in East Dorset there is a complete sequence, including Portland and Purbeck Beds, Wealden, Lower Greensand, Gault and Upper Greensand, we find the Gault transgressing westward on to lower and lower strata, as is shown diagrammatically in *Fig.* 4.

W   E

FIG. 4. THE CRETACEOUS OVERSTEP.
(Diagrammatic.)

The Cretaceous Beds rest on Bathonian to the east of Bridport, on Lias at Charmouth, while in Devon they overstep on to the Trias. Clearly the Jurassic rocks had been tilted and eroded before the sea transgressed over their denuded edges in Albian times, while more recent erosion has re-exposed them. There is here a great unconformity therefore.

In the transgressive Albian sea the first deposit formed was a grey clayey sand, the **Gault,** with a pebbly base. Gault fossils may be found in it near the top of Black Ven and Stonebarrow. Still Albian in age is the so-called **Upper Greensand,** with fossils characteristic of the Upper Gault of Folkestone. The lower part may contain hard sandstone con-

* From Bayeux, in Normandy.
† From Aalen, in Württemberg.
‡ From Vesoul, Haute-Saône.

cretions, called Cowstones; the middle is a sand, the Fox-mould; and above come chert beds. Foxmould, however, like gault, is a local term not restricted to one geological horizon, and the Dorset man who is not a geologist calls the Bridport Sand foxmould.

The chert of the Upper Greensand owes its silica to the spicules of siliceous sponges that grew on the sea floor. To a similar source may be attributed the flint nodules in the **Chalk**, the next deposit. The Chalk sea had much the same western boundary as the Liassic sea, but eastward it stretched through Germany and Russia to the Caspian region. Chalk zones up to that of *Micraster cor-testudinarium* are exposed in the cliffs west of Lyme Regis.

Deposits of known Eocene age are not found in West Dorset, but relics of Eocene beds may be incorporated in the **Clay-with-flints** that covers most of the Cretaceous uplands. The solution of the Chalk by rain water, which left the insoluble flints and clay that form the bulk of the Clay-with-flints, may also have commenced in Eocene times.

There is little of Pleistocene age in the area, though Mammoth has been recorded at Charmouth; and Recent deposits of rivers or sea are also of trifling extent. Long-continued sub-aerial erosion has cut valleys through the Chalk down to the Jurassic rocks, and marine erosion, truncating those valleys and their intervening ridges, has given rise to the diversified coastline we see to-day.

Only small streams drain the area—indeed, there is no river of consequence between the Axe and the Frome. The Lym is a juvenile stream with a narrow, steep-sided valley and a steep gradient, which has been utilised for mills. The Char has an open, mature valley, the broad Vale of Marshwood, floored with clays of the Lower Lias and flanked by hills of Upper Greensand and Chalk, which are the source of most of its streams. The Brit too has its source in the Upper Greensand at Beaminster. Two tributaries, the Symene and the Asker, join it at Bridport. The Bride (or Bredy, *cf.* Bidëford) rises in Chalk and flows westward along a strike-line; it was, no doubt, a tributary of the Brit before the coast receded.

Lyme Regis and West Bay (Bridport Harbour) are the only towns or villages on the coast of West Dorset, if we except the few houses at Seatown. Charmouth and Eype lie half-a-mile inland, Bridport a mile and three-quarters. Lyme Regis is a good place for the study of the Lower Lias, but Bridport is a very much better centre, with good bus services west, east and north.

DRAW

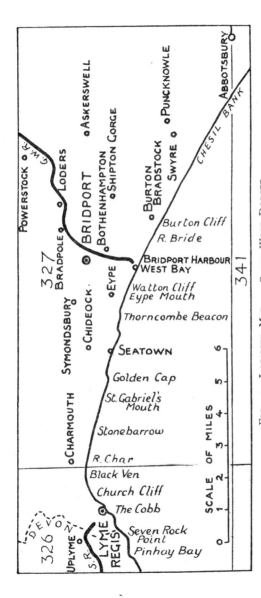

Fig. 5. Locality Map of South-West Dorset.
Scale : 1 inch to 3 miles.
Showing boundaries of the one-inch maps of the Geological Survey Sheets 326, 327, 341.

SUGGESTED EXCURSIONS IN WESTERN DORSET

Assuming Bridport is chosen for headquarters, the following suggested programme shows what can be done in a week. The state of the tide must be taken into consideration (p. 2), and the routes varied accordingly, or even reversed. Many of these routes may be taken equally well from Lyme Regis.

FIRST DAY. LOWER LIAS OF LYME REGIS

By road to Lyme Regis, nine miles west. Walk westward to the beginning of the landslip, and descend to the shore by the fault in Pinhay Bay. Walk back to Lyme Regis along the shore, examining the White Lias and Blue Lias in cliff and ledges.

Continue eastward under Church Cliffs and Black Ven to the mouth of the Char; or examine the terraces of Black Ven. Return by road from Charmouth. Walking distance, six miles (pp. 15-26).

SECOND DAY. LOWER AND MIDDLE LIAS BETWEEN CHARMOUTH AND SEATOWN

By road to Charmouth, seven miles west. Walk down to the shore and eastward below Stonebarrow and Golden Cap. The cliffs show Black Ven Marls, Belemnite Marls, Green Ammonite Beds, the Three Tiers at the base of the Middle Lias, Eype Clay, Down Cliff Sands and Thorncombe Sands, with Upper Greensand capping both Stonebarrow and Golden Cap. Walk back from Seatown to Bridport by cliff and field-paths; or return by road from Chideock. Walking distance, six miles (pp. 26-30).

THIRD DAY. WATTON CLIFF AND EAST CLIFF, BRIDPORT

Walk to Eype Mouth and eastward to the fault corner. Examine the Junction Bed, Forest Marble and Fuller's Earth. Continue along the shore to West Bay, and below East Cliff, where fossils may be collected from fallen masses of Inferior Oolite which overlies the Bridport Sands. Walk back over East Cliff and by path to Bridport. Walking distance, seven miles (pp. 32-36).

FOURTH DAY. BURTON CLIFF, BURTON BRADSTOCK, AND BOTHENHAMPTON

By road to West Bay. Walk over the East Cliff and beneath Burton Cliff, where the whole of the Inferior Oolite caps the Bridport Sands. Walk northward through Burton Bradstock to the Bridport Brick and Tile Works (Kellaways Clay), and west to Bothenhampton (Forest Marble) and Bridport. Walking distance, seven miles (pp. 36-39).

FIFTH DAY. INFERIOR OOLITE OF LODERS CROSS AND SHIPTON GORGE

By road to Loders Cross, three miles east. Visit quarries in Inferior Oolite here and at Vinney Cross. Thence take footpath to the top of Shipton Hill, an outlier of Upper Greensand and a good view-point. Then down to Shipton Gorge and Peas Hill quarry opposite the New Inn, where microzoa are abundant in the upper part of the Inferior Oolite. Walk on by lane and path, over the hills above Bothenhampton to Bridport. Walking distance, five miles. This would make a good introductory half-day on arrival at Bridport. See Richardson, 1928-30, for details and map.

SIXTH DAY. CRETACEOUS AND INFERIOR OOLITE NEAR BEAMINSTER

By road to Beaminster, six miles north. Walk north to Buckham Down, visiting exposures in Upper Greensand on either side of the lane. Walk west by road crossing tunnel at Horn Hill, near which an old pit shows fossiliferous Upper Greensand and Chloritic Marl. One mile farther west, turn south to Waddon Hill, above Stoke Knap, with quarries in Inferior Oolite. Then eastward to Horn Park quarry on the Broadwindsor-Beaminster road, where the same rock is crowded with ammonites. Return by road from Beaminster. Walking distance, seven miles (p. 40 and Richardson, 1928-30).

SEVENTH DAY. INFERIOR OOLITE EAST OF YEOVIL

By road (or rail) to Yeovil, twenty miles north, and Halfway House on the Yeovil-Sherborne road. Visit quarries here and at Louse Hill and Bradford Abbas to the south. The best quarries at Bradford, however, have been filled in or planted. A quarry in Fuller's Earth Rock may be visited near Thornford, and the return to Yeovil may be made by Bradford Hollow Way between banks of Yeovil Sand. Walking distance, eight miles (see Richardson, 1932, for details and map).

PINHAY BAY TO LYME REGIS
(2 miles. Six-inch map, Dorset 36 S.E.)

County boundaries have little geological significance, and we will begin our survey of the Dorset coast at Pinhay Bay, a mile west of the Devon-Dorset boundary. It may be reached from Lyme Regis by walking along the shore westward from the Cobb; or by way of Broad Street, Pound Street, and the footpath to Ware Cliff. This path joins a lane for 400 yards near Underhill Farm, then runs westward for three-quarters of a mile to a tiny stream that falls into Pinhay Bay. Here turn left and descend to the shore by steps cut in the cliff on the S.W. side of the Pinhay Bay fault.

The main path may be continued nearly to Seaton through a great series of landslips. They are backed by cliffs of Upper Greensand and Chalk, reaching 400 or 500 feet above sea level, below which is a jumble of slipped Cretaceous, Liassic, Rhætic and Keuper rocks. One big fall occurred near Dowlands in December, 1839, when some forty acres subsided toward the sea, leaving a chasm half a mile long and from 130 to 210 feet deep, and ridging up the sea-bottom into a reef, which, however, was soon eroded. This occurrence was due, not to an earthquake as reported at the time, but to a heavy rainfall that lubricated the seaward-dipping surface of Triassic marls beneath the permeable Cretaceous rocks. Full

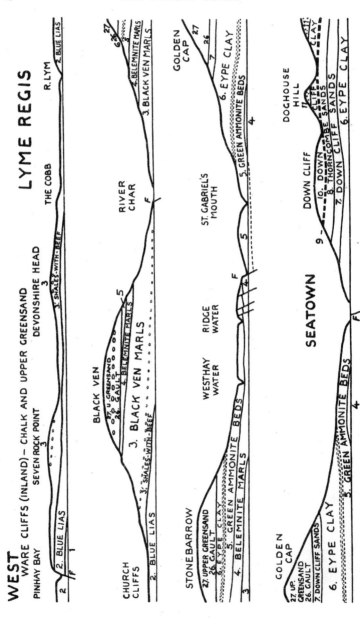

WEST
WARE CLIFFS (INLAND) – CHALK AND UPPER GREENSAND

LYME REGIS

PINHAY BAY
SEVEN ROCK POINT
DEVONSHIRE HEAD
THE COBB
R. LYM

2. BLUE LIAS
2. BLUE LIAS
3. SHALES-WITH-BEEF
2. BLUE LIAS

CHURCH
CLIFFS
BLACK VEN
27. U. GREENSAND
26. GAULT
4. BELEMNITE MARLS
3. BLACK VEN MARLS
3. SHALES-WITH-BEEF

RIVER
CHAR
27
6 26
7
4. BELEMNITE MARLS
3. BLACK VEN MARLS

GOLDEN
CAP
27
26
7
6. EYPE CLAY
5. GREEN AMMONITE BEDS

STONEBARROW
WESTHAY
WATER
RIDGE
WATER
ST. GABRIEL'S
MOUTH

27. UPPER GREENSAND
26. GAULT
6. EYPE CLAY
5. GREEN AMMONITE BEDS
4. BELEMNITE MARLS

SEATOWN
DOWN CLIFF
DOGHOUSE
HILL

GOLDEN
CAP
27. UP.
GREENSAND
26. GAULT
7. DOWN CLIFF SANDS
6. EYPE CLAY
5. GREEN AMMONITE BEDS

10. DOWN
8. THORNCOMBE SANDS
7. DOWN CLIFF SANDS
6. EYPE CLAY
11
11. CLIFF
CLAY

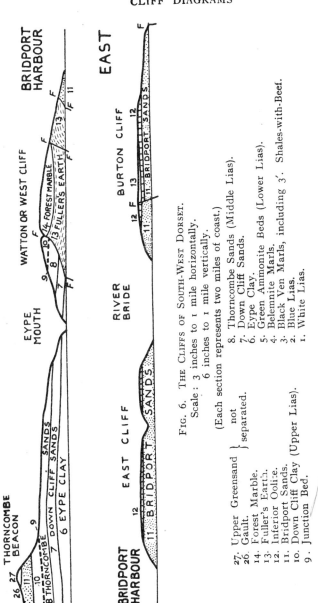

FIG. 6. THE CLIFFS OF SOUTH-WEST DORSET.

Scale: 3 inches to 1 mile horizontally.

6 inches to 1 mile vertically.

(Each section represents two miles of coast.)

27. Upper Greensand ⎰ not
26. Gault.   ⎱ separated.
14. Forest Marble.
13. Fuller's Earth.
12. Inferior Oolite.
11. Bridport Sands.
10. Down Cliff Clay (Upper Lias).
 9. Junction Bed.

 8. Thorncombe Sands (Middle Lias).
 7. Down Cliff Sands.
 6. Eype Clay.
 5. Green Ammonite Beds (Lower Lias).
 4. Belemnite Marls.
 3. Black Ven Marls, including 3'. Shales-with-Beef.
 2. Blue Lias.
 1. White Lias.

accounts of this " mighty land-slip," were given by W. D. Conybeare and G. Roberts, in 1840*.

On reaching the shore at **Pinhay Bay**, note first the **fault** along which the little stream already mentioned has eroded a gully. To the eastward, the White Lias is clearly distinguished from the overlying Blue Lias, the junction being about 10 feet above the base of the cliff. South-west of the fault the top of the White Lias is thrown down some 40 feet and may be seen between high and low water marks.

Walking eastward along the shore, we are on **White Lias** for the first 600 yards. It is a thin-bedded white limestone and is seldom fossiliferous. Black Shales with *Pteria* (*Avicula*) *contorta* occur near low water mark.

The White Lias is followed by the **Blue Lias,** which forms the main part of the cliffs of Pinhay Bay and the foreshore between Pinhay Bay and Black Ven. It is also known as the Lyme Regis Beds. It consists of alternations of limestone and shale, and is the most typical portion of the " Lias," the rock that occurs in layers†.

The actual base of the Blue Lias is not so readily detected on the spot as from a distance. It is taken at a band of thin brown paper-shales with films of limestone, which is locally crowded with echinoderm spines. It is followed by some 10 feet of thin limestones separated by shales. These yield no ammonites, but species of oyster are common; they are known as the *Ostrea* beds.

Above the main stone beds of the Blue Lias come some 12 feet of shale and then an isolated band of limestone known as Table Ledge. This limestone is taken as the top of the Blue Lias; it may usually be seen at the top of the cliff, the overlying Shales-with-Beef having weathered back to a gentler slope.

In former times the limestones on the shore were quarried for cement-making and for road-stones and paving slabs, a reprehensible custom that increased the rate of coast-erosion and has now fortunately been abandoned. The quarrymen had their own names for the different limestones they worked, such as Table Ledge and Grey Ledge, which explain themselves, or Rattle, Mongrel, and Gumption, which do not. The whole of the coastal outcrop of the Blue Lias, from Pinhay Bay to Black Ven, has been described in detail and mapped

---

* For references see pp. 113-122.
† The alternative derivations, from the French *liais,* a fine-grained limestone, or Gaelic *leac,* a flat stone, seem improbable. The term " Lyas " was used in Somerset as early as 1719.

on the scale of 25 inches to the mile by W. D. Lang (1914 and 1924), and the following abstract is based on his work. The four zones adopted by Oppel and the Geological Survey were replaced in Lang's account by thirteen zones. These were based on ammonite sequences determined elsewhere by Spath, but as most of the zonal ammonites are not known in Dorset their utility is doubtful. The hemeræ or faunal horizons proposed by Buckman and Tutcher (1918) did not exactly correspond with them.

DETAILS OF THE BLUE LIAS

	Limestones.		Shales.	
	ft.	in.	ft.	in.
Zone of *Arnioceras semicostatum* (13 feet).				
Table Ledge	1	0		
Shales, some with " beef," including the Saurian Bed and the Fish Bed			12	0
Zone of *Ammonites* (*s.s.,* = *Coroniceras*) *bucklandi* (37 feet).				
Grey Ledge, and shales beneath	5			7
Glass Bottle, and shales	10		2	7
Top Quick, and shales	9		1	5
Venty, and shales	6		6	0
Best Bed, and shales	7			7
Second Bed, and shales	8		1	1
Rattle, and shales	6		3	6
Second Quick, and shales	11			4
Gumption, and shales	3		4	2
Third Quick, and shales	1	0	1	7
Top Tape, and shales	10			10
Second Tape, and shales	9			2
Top Copper, and shales	3			7
Mongrel, and shales	8		1	0
Second Mongrel, and shales	3			8
Specketty, and shales	1	0	1	6
Upper White, and shales	6			4
Zone of *Schlotheimia angulata* (25 feet).				
Upper Skulls, and shales	8			2
Iron Ledge, and shales	7			6
Under Copper, and shales	5			6
Under White, or Third Tape, and shales	6			4
Lower Skulls, and shales	8			11
Lower Venty, and shales	3			3
Pig's Dirt, or Soft Bed, and shales	3			2
Brick Ledge (six thin limestones), and shales ...	2	6		8
18 un-named limestones and shales	4	9	10	7
Zone of *Psiloceras planorbis* (20 feet).				
27 un-named limestones and shales	9	4	10	5

The beds below Brick Ledge run out to sea near Seven Rock Point and are not seen nearer Lyme Regis. They were

not worked for cement, and have not received distinctive
names. Brick Ledge itself is made up of six thin limestones
and, with nine similar limestones below it, forms a conspicuous
band, about 8 feet thick, of fifteen thin limestones with
undulating surfaces. This band is easily seen in the cliff; with
a gentle easterly dip it swings across the foreshore at Seven
Rock Point and forms a reef at low water with a steep face to
the west.

For some 15 feet above Brick Ledge the limestones are
separated by thin bands of shale only. Lower Skulls is a pair
of thin regular wavy limestones, 2 feet above Brick Ledge,
well seen at the base of the cliff at Seven Rock Point. Iron
Ledge comes 2¼ feet higher and is followed by Upper Skulls,
which also is usually in two layers, nodular, with frequent
Schlotheimia spp. Specketty, 2¼ feet higher, is a strong,
regular limestone, and 2 feet above it is Mongrel, easily recognised by its undulating
upper surface which forms
a ledge on the shore full
of deep puddles. Top
Tape is divided in two by
a film of shale, and is
crowded with *Vermiceras*.

Above Top Tape the
limestones are more widely-
spaced. Third Quick
(quarrymen and miners
generally count beds from
the surface downward) is about 2 feet above Top Tape and is
full of *Gryphæa*. The thin Gumption is only 4 inches below
Second Quick, while 4 feet of shale separate them from Third
Quick below and Rattle above. Rattle, Second Bed and Best
Bed form a conspicuous threefold band. Above 6 feet of shale
come Venty and Top Quick, and then Glass Bottle. Grey
Ledge is impersistent, so that locally Glass Bottle may be the
highest of the stone beds proper. Table Ledge is separated
from them by at least 12 feet of shale.

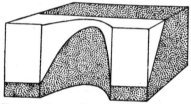

FIG. 7. BLOCK DIAGRAM SHOWING AN
APPARENT ANTICLINE
in a bay cut in strata with a constant
dip to seaward.

All these beds may be seen in the cliffs of Pinhay Bay.
The general dip to the E. or S.E. brings them all down to sea
level before the Cobb is reached, but not quite in a regular
sequence. Even where there is a uniform dip to seaward,
irregularities in the coast-line will give the appearance of
changes in dip; a bay will cut back into lower beds and suggest
an anticline, while a projection will suggest an equally non-

existent syncline (see *Fig.* 7). But here there really are minor folds.

In Pinhay Bay, where the shore is clear of loose stones, we seem to be continually going upstairs in walking eastward, but without getting any higher. The " risers " are the little escarpments of the limestones, undercut by the more rapid erosion of the shales, but the " treads " are the limestone surfaces, which dip eastward. So, while steadily attaining higher geological horizons, our height above sea-level remains about the same.

The curvative of the reefs at Seven Rock Point indicates the nose of an elongated dome. Just east of the point, the complementary syncline or basin is crossed, Rattle Shales appearing at the foot of the cliff with Rattle running along-shore near low-water mark. Then another dome-like anti-cline, with its centre near Devonshire Head, brings up lower beds in succession down to Brick Ledge, and the limestones here form convenient promenades parallel to the shore and curving inland at the ends of the dome.

Beyond Chippel Bay a wide and gentle syncline brings the stone beds of the Blue Lias down below the old cement works. The Cobb is founded on them. They run beneath the Esplanade and a short distance up the valley of the Lym, and rise to view once more in Church Cliff. The overlying Shales-with-Beef and the rest of the Black Ven Marls form the slopes on which Lyme Regis stands. From the Cobb a good view may be had of the coast eastward to Bridport, and sometimes to Portland Bill. The Cobb is built of Cowstones from the Upper Greensand with a walling of Portland Roach in which casts of *Cerithium* and *Trigonia* are well seen.

LYME REGIS TO CHARMOUTH
(1½ miles. Six-inch map, Dorset 37 S.W.)

The cliffs immediately N.E. of Lyme Regis are known as Church Cliffs. They are formed of the higher beds of the Blue Lias, and so is the broad belt of reefs below. Broad Ledge, south-east of St. Michael's Church, is about the horizon of Third Quick. The bedding here is horizontal. It marks the crest of an anticline, for Second Quick may be seen dipping W. in Long Ledge and below the easternmost jetty, and dipping E. in Snag's Ledge. This, the Church Cliffs anticline, causes the lower limestones to form ring-like outcrops on the shore some 300 yards N.E. of the church. Third Quick is the outermost of these rings seen at the south-west end of the dome. Lower beds down to Brick Ledge are brought up in succession as the anticlinal axis enters the cliff, but the outcrops are much obscured by shingle and debris from the cliff above.

Outside this area of beach, the limestones form more or less continuous reefs parallel to the shore-line but swinging round at the N.E. end of the dome. The reefs are followed by a muddy patch of shore known as the Cockpits, where a little syncline is clearly seen at low tide, the top of the stone beds dipping S.E. on one side and N.W. on the other. Grey Ledge is repeated by faulting in Canary Ledges, and is cut off by another fault. Table Ledge is seen, also faulted, in Black Ven Rocks. It dips eastward, and so the Blue Lias is carried down out of sight.

The overlying **Black Ven Marls** have now descended to shore-level. It is to their dark colour that Black Ven owes its name. *Ven* is a local form of *fen* and alludes to the boggy nature of the Black Ven terraces.

Above Table Ledge come some 70 feet of dark shales with thin bands of calcite which show a fibrous structure faintly resembling that of beef-steak. They are called " beef," and this lower part of the Black Ven Marls is known as the **Shales-with-Beef.** The calcite has evidently segregated from a slightly calcareous mud, but it has formed crystals growing from opposite sides of a bedding-plane. A parting of shaly matter occurs in the centre of each vein. The simple fibrous structure is complicated by cone-in-cone structure, which developed as the crystals grew against the pressure of the overlying mass. Paper-shales are conspicuous in places in the cliff; their fine lamination seems to be due to the development of minute crystals of selenite in the bedding-planes as a result of weathering. Pyritic nodules occur, and small discs of barytes have been noted.

The reefs known as Bar Ledges, Raffey's Ledge and Little Ledge are formed of " beef " bands, which do not appear to have much persistence. This is the best place to see the fossils of the Shales-with-Beef, mostly species of *Arnioceras, Lima, Avicula, Ostrea, Rhynchonella,* etc. Little collecting can be done in the cliff, where these beds form the lowest of the three clay precipices of Black Ven, with the *birchi* nodules as a capping. The shelf above is easily accessible from Spittles Lane, Lyme Regis, and it was at its western end that the burning cliff, or " **Lyme volcano,**" was situated. In 1908 the rapid oxidation of iron-pyrites in a fallen mass of Black Ven Marls generated sufficient heat to cause combustion in the

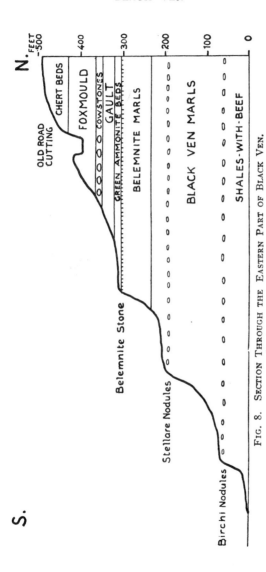

FIG. 8. SECTION THROUGH THE EASTERN PART OF BLACK VEN.

Scale : 2 feet to 1 mile.

Farther west the Gault oversteps the Green Ammonite Beds and rests on the Belemnite Marls.

pyritic and slightly bituminous shales. Clouds of smoke were evolved and the shales were burnt to the appearance of red tiles; but it is said that when the " volcano " showed signs of subsiding it was stimulated with paraffin (H. B. Woodward, 1908, W. D. Lang, 1909). A burning rubbish dump now forms an appropriate monument to the Lyme volcano. Similar " eruptions " occurred near Charmouth in 1751, at Golden Cap in 1890, and in the Kimmeridge Clay of Holworth Cliff in 1826-29.

The Shales-with-Beef extend upward to a band of large calcareous nodules followed by a tabular limestone, both of which yield well-preserved specimens of *Microderoceras birchi,* known locally as the tortoise ammonites or white ammonites, from the white calcite that often fills their chambers. The *birchi* nodules were sometimes called cement-stones (the building nearest the sea at Charmouth is an old cement-mill), and also firestone nodules from having been used as fuel-economisers. They form the lowest terrace on Black Ven and descend to sea-level at the mouth of the Char. Here a small fault with a downthrow of about 10 feet to the east (W. D. Lang, 1932) is accompanied by some intense crumpling of the beds on either side, and the tabular limestone above the *birchi* nodules is seen in the Mouth Rocks, first dipping steeply eastward and then brought up in three sharp anticlines. The fault runs up the western side of the Char valley, but is generally hidden by beach. Two small faults may be seen in the cliff opposite Bar Ledges.

The middle clay precipice on Black Ven includes the **Black Ven Marls** above the *birchi* nodules and up to the *stellare* nodules and the Coinstone limestone, which form another terrace. The succession of shales and clays is broken by thin bands of harder material, not always very persistent. Of these the Lower Cement Bed is about 40 feet above the *Birchi* Bed, and Pavior (the Upper Cement Bed of Woodward) comes 15 feet higher. A conspicuous band of paper-shales follows, containing *Asteroceras obtusum* and lines of nodules, the Flatstones and Woodstone. The Pentacrinite Bed, with the crinoid *Extracrinus briareus,* and a limestone crowded with *Promicroceras planicosta,* the equivalent of the ammonite-marble of Marston Magna, are both impersistent. The Mudstone is a more constant horizon; it contains small nodules, sometimes with zinc-blende. Seven feet higher is a limestone with brachiopods, conspicuous by reason of the yellow colour it assumes on weathering, and above that are the nodules with *Asteroceras stellare* and the limestone called the Coinstone. These form the second terrace on Black Ven.

Six feet above the *stellare* nodules is a band of beef and iron pyrites with well-preserved ammonites, the *lymense* bed, and 25 feet higher comes the Watch Ammonite Stone, a limestone with ammonites of the *Echioceras raricostatum* type. The top of the Black Ven Marls is reached 12 feet above this, in a thin limestone known as Hummocky. Iron-pyrites is abundant in these beds; it gives the name of Metal Bed to one band and it was formerly collected for the manufacture of sulphuric acid. The clays above the Coinstone are poorly exposed and generally covered by talus at the foot of the third precipice.

The main part of the upper clay precipice at Black Ven consists of the pale grey **Belemnite Marls,** capped by a thin limestone, the Belemnite Stone, where not overstepped by the Gault. The light colour contrasts with that of the Black Ven Marls, and the greater permeability of the Belemnite Marls results in springs being thrown out at their base, causing the terrace below them to be very boggy. They are better seen farther east, at Stonebarrow and on the shore below Golden Cap. Belemnites in great abundance and variety occur in these beds. In some examples even the ink-sacs have been preserved, and the sepia has been used for drawings, according to Buckland in his Bridgewater Treatise of 1836. Small pyritised ammonites, near *Acanthopleuroceras valdani,* are also common. At the base of the Belemnite Marls Lang places the upper part of the limestone called Hummocky, with *Epideroceras exheredatum.* One foot above this is the *armatus* limestone, with *Apoderoceras leckenbyi.*

A wedge of the lower part of the **Green Ammonite Beds,** truncated by the Gault, occurs in the eastern part of Black Ven. It includes, however, the nodules containing *Androgynoceras latæcosta,* infilled with greenish calcite, the '' green ammonites '' that give these clays their name.

The **Cretaceous** beds that overstep these Lower Lias strata at the top of Black Ven have long been known as '' Gault '' and '' Upper Greensand.'' They are all of Albian age and therefore Gault in the stratigraphic sense although not gault in the textural sense of a stiff clay. Their base is about 320 feet above sea-level, and is very wet owing to the water thrown out by the Liassic clays below. There is a thin basal pebble bed in which water-worn Liassic fossils occur, followed by some 40 feet of loam and loamy sand. These constitute the **Gault** of Jukes-Browne and the zone of

c

Hoplites interruptus of Lang. The commonest fossils are *Pecten orbicularis, Lima parallela, Inoceramus concentricus,* and *Serpula concava,* while the ammonites *Anahoplites præcox* and *A. intermedius* show a Lower Gault (Middle Albian) age. Fossils are commonest in a blue micaceous loam, Bed 3 of Lang.

The "**Upper Greensand**" has three divisions, the Cowstones below, followed by the Foxmould and the Chert Beds. The Cowstones are hard, tough sandstone concretions lying in three bands in 20 feet of grey sand. They contain Upper Gault fossils, including *Hysteroceras varicosum.* Then come 70 feet or more of grey, yellow or brown sand, the Foxmould, through which passes the old road from Lyme to Charmouth which was closed owing to subsidence about 1923. Fragments of *Mortoniceras* show that both the Foxmould and the Chert Beds are of Upper Gault age. *Exogyra conica* and *Pecten quadricostatus* are commoner fossils, and are often found with the shells replaced by beekite, a rosette-like form of silica.

The Chert Beds here are mere broken remnants and pass up into a brown Drift containing fragments of chert and unworn flints from the Chalk.

CHARMOUTH TO SEATOWN
(3½ miles. Six-inch maps, Dorset 37 S.W., 37 S.E.)

This stretch of coast passes beneath the hills of Stonebarrow on the west and Golden Cap on the east. It will be convenient to describe Stonebarrow first, then the traverse along the shore, and finally Golden Cap.

The lowest precipice at Stonebarrow shows the **Black Ven Marls** below the *stellare* nodules, which form a terrace here as at Black Ven. The nodules appear in the cliff at about 100 feet O.D. in the Vineyard and descend to the shore about half a mile farther east. The topmost beds of the Black Ven Marls are generally masked by slips and talus.

The second precipice consists of the **Belemnite Marls** or Stonebarrow Beds, 75 feet of pale grey marl. They are well exposed in the gullies, where the harder bands give rise to little waterfalls, but they can be examined more conveniently where they descend to shore-level farther east. The Belemnite Stone, a hard whitish limestone crowded with belemnites, tops the second precipice.

The **Green Ammonite Beds** have weathered back to a gentler slope, but only the lower part is well exposed below Stonebarrow. They are 50 feet thick here, and the succession of clays is broken by three indurated bands, 10, 20, and 35 feet above the Belemnite Stone. Eastward, the clays thicken, and below Golden Cap each of these divisions is double the thickness, the whole measuring 100 feet or more.

The lowest of these indurated bands, the Lower Limestone, consists of hard nodules. The middle one is the conspicuous Red Band, an impure and slightly ferruginous limestone. The third, the Upper Limestone, is sometimes flaggy, sometimes nodular, and not so easily found. Fragments of *Androgynoceras latæcosta* are common in the lower clays. *Liparoceras dædalicosta* is found in the middle part, and *Oistoceras* in the upper, while *Tragophylloceras loscombi* is common throughout.

The **Middle Lias** makes its appearance on the west side of Stonebarrow at about 250 feet above sea-level. Only the lowest member, the **Eype Clay** (Blue Clay, or *Margaritatus* Marls) appears, with the three bands of fissile micaceous sandstone, known as the **Three Tiers**, at the base. The Three Tiers may be seen in the cliff above the Fairy Dell (or Cain's Folly), and fallen blocks on the slopes of the Green Ammonite Beds may be split up in search of fossils. *Tragophylloceras loscombi* is still common, but it is now accompanied by the Domerian ammonite *Amaltheus margaritatus*.

As at Black Ven, the base of the **Gault** is not far above the 300-foot contour line; sections may be seen in the upper part of the Fairy Dell. Cowstones are not developed in the **Upper Greensand** here or farther east. The top of the hill is covered with Drift containing chert and flints.

We now descend to the shore. Up to the beginning of this century the River Char, when only a hundred yards from the sea, meandered from the eastern to the western side of its valley and back, entering the sea under the eastern cliffs or percolating through the shingle. This pushing of a river-mouth eastward, through the easterly drift of shingle, is a common phenomenon on the south coast; the Exe and the Otter show it well. In the hope of keeping the mouth permanently open, the neck of the meander was cut through and the river extension beneath the cliffs was dammed, giving a direct course to the sea. Now the northern reach of the artificially cut-off meander remains as a marsh, the southern reach is choked with shingle, and the river is cutting into the meander-core between them. Beneath the shingle lie the remains of a submerged forest, with drifted birch, ash and hazel-nuts, and antlers of Red Deer (Lang, 1926). De la Beche records remains of Mammoth, *Elephas primigenius,* presumably from an underlying gravel.

A small fault runs down the Char valley and is associated with the sharp anticlines in the *birchi* bed at Mouth Rocks (p. 24). To the same movement are due the contortions in the **Black Ven Marls** seen in the first low cliff east of the river. Farther east the contortions pass into gentle undulations, but there is a general westerly dip for the first half-mile. The Lower Cement Bed may be seen rising from beach-level, and, as the cliff attains a greater height, the *stellare* nodules appear at the top of the first precipice. On the normal easterly dip being resumed, these beds are seen to descend to sea-level, the Lower Cement Bed forming the Black Rock reef, Pavior (Woodward's Upper Cement Bed) Dover Ledge, and the *stellare* Bed the Mumbles.

The highest beds of the Black Ven Marls are sometimes well exposed in the cliff about one mile east of Charmouth. They appear to be thicker here than on Black Ven; Lang in 1914 noted 51 feet of clays between the Coinstone and the *Apoderoceras* (" *armatus* ") limestone.

The pale grey **Belemnite Marls** now form the seaward cliffs and may be easily examined. They have been called the Stonebarrow Beds by H. B. Woodward. The small pyritised ammonites, *Uptonia bronni,* abound in the lower part, and *Tropidoceras ellipticum,* also pyritised, in the upper; they may be picked up at the base of the shingle, where the waves have concentrated the heavy pyritic material. They are very unstable, breaking down to masses of melanterite ($FeSO_4.7H_2O$), but their life may be prolonged if they are first soaked in water to remove any salt and acid material, and then coated with shellac dissolved in alcohol or celluloid dissolved in amyl acetate.

The *Apoderoceras* limestone at the base of the Belemnite Marls forms a long ridge crossing the foreshore beneath the shingle, and the indurated marls immediately above it are seen in Hawkfish Ledge, a reef opposite the point where Westhay Water makes a cliff-waterfall. Instead of running out to sea, this reef runs along the shore for 300 yards; the easterly dip here flattens out, and later reverses.

The Belemnite Stone caps the cliffs, the Green Ammonite Beds above sloping back at a gentler angle. Beyond Ridge Water, the second cliff-waterfall, the dip becomes westerly, but it is counteracted by three small step-faults with downthrows to the east. Then the cliff ends in a fourth fault, itself double, which throws the Belemnite Marls down in two steps of 50 feet each, below sea-level. The face of this important Ridge fault is seen as a fault-scarp, the clays of the Green

Ammonite Beds on the downthrow side having weathered back faster than the Belemnite Marls with their protective capping of Belemnite Stone. The Red Band in the former series may be found, just east of the fault-scarp, thrown down to the level of the Belemnite Stone, while a few yards farther east it has been thrown down to the foreshore.

From the Ridge fault to St. Gabriel's Mouth lies a rough tract of sloped and slipped **Green Ammonite Beds.** The dip is still westerly, and the Red Band may be traced, as a double red band, rising from the foreshore to a height of 40 feet in Wear Cliffs, beyond St. Gabriel's Mouth, where the dip again becomes easterly. The Belemnite Stone and Marls also rise to the base of the cliff in this anticline, and occur in the foreshore most of the way round the point and on to Seatown.

In Wear Cliffs even the Green Ammonite Beds have a precipitous outcrop, thanks to rapid marine erosion at the foot of the cliff. South and south-east of Golden Cap the normal clay-slope is renewed. These beds continue in the undercliff as far east as Seatown, where they are faulted down below sea-level, and with them the Lower Lias disappears from the Dorset coast.

The overlying **Three Tiers** are well seen in Wear Cliffs, where they form ledges and waterfalls, and fallen blocks of these micaceous sandstones are strewn over the shore below, resting on Belemnite Marls in the Western Patches and around Little Cann, where they help to protect the point from wave-action. The Three Tiers do not form a precise boundary between Lower and Middle Lias, for Lang (1932) states that *Amaltheus* occurs 11 feet beneath them, in a series of loams forming a transition from the clays with *Oistoceras* to the marls with *Amaltheus margaritatus*. The lowest Tier is about 4 feet thick, the other two only half that thickness, and they are separated by 10 or 12 feet of micaceous sandy clay.

About 100 feet above the Three Tiers is a nodular band of calcareous sandy rock, but the bluish Eype Clay continues for another 60 feet, up to the Starfish Bed. The lower part of the **Down Cliff Sands** (or Laminated Beds) is also present, the rest being cut off by the Cretaceous overstep.

About 30 feet of grey sandy clays with Lower Gault fossils are followed by the yellow sands, the Foxmould, that give Golden Cap its name.

The return from Seatown to Charmouth may be made over the top of Golden Cap (619 feet) and Stonebarrow (484 feet), with views that may extend from Tor Bay to Portland Bill. It is a waste of energy to try to follow the cliff top all the way; landslips and landlords are alike obstructive. The better way is to descend from Golden Cap to the ruined Church of St. Gabriel, cross the valley by a path leading to Upcot, then turn left and follow a track by Ridge Barn and Westhay Farm to Stonebarrow and the cliff path down to the mouth of the Char, or direct to Newlands Bridge and the village of Charmouth.

SEATOWN TO EYPE MOUTH
(2 miles. Six-inch maps, Dorset 37 S.E., 38 S.W.)

The fault at Seatown has a downthrow to the east of nearly 200 feet, but it is nowhere exposed. Its effect is to throw the Lower Lias, the Three Tiers, and the lower part of the Eype Clay down below sea-level, and they are not seen again in the cliffs. Buckman (1922) states that the Three Tiers form the Ledges on the foreshore beneath the eastern end of Thorncombe Beacon. In Down Cliff*, Doghouse Hill and Thorncombe Beacon, the upper part of the Eype Clay is seen above the talus at the foot of the cliffs, and large blocks from the overlying Starfish Bed are strewn on the slope and beach. This bed is seen in the cliff, at a height of from 90 to 35 feet from the base, undulating, but on the whole dipping gently eastward. It is a band of micaceous sandstone, 4 ft. 6 in. thick. Where the smooth lower surface is exposed, as in fallen blocks, remains of the starfishes, *Ophioderma egertoni* and *O. tenuibrachiata,* may be seen; but local collectors are active in chiselling them out.

Above the Starfish Bed come the **Down Cliff Sands** (or Laminated Beds), some 70 feet of micaceous sandy clays and sands, with a thin sandy limestone near the middle.

At the top of the Down Cliff Sands, and some 160 feet from the base of Down Cliff, a conspicuous reddish-brown band is seen. This is the weathered outcrop of a hard blue sandy limestone, the *Margaritatus* Stone, about one foot thick. Fossils may be collected from fallen blocks. It is followed by sandy clay and then by yellow sands, which are often cemented into hard concretions, or doggers. More sandy clays follow, in which *Paltopleuroceras spinatum* takes the place of *Amaltheus margaritatus* as the zonal fossil. The whole of the beds, some 70 feet thick, between the Down Cliff Sands and

---

* Also known as Ridge Cliff, from its form. There is another Ridge Cliff 2¼ miles to the westward, below Ridge Barn.

the Junction Bed are included under the name of the **Thorncombe Sands** (Yellow Sands or Middle Lias Sands).

The **Junction Bed**, so-called from combining in a single block of limestone deposits of Middle and Upper· Liassic age, is generally about 3 feet thick in these cliffs. It represents in a condensed sequence deposits which in Yorkshire are over 300 feet thick. The slow accumulation of limestone was broken by many periods of erosion, some of which are represented by wavy lines in the table below. This is shown by erosion planes which may remove the upper parts of fossils, and by the presence of rolled ammonites and pebbles of the same type of limestone, sometimes bored by *Lithophagus*. The limestone must have been a hard stone, and not a soft ooze, before it could be so eroded. The top of the Junction Bed is another plane of erosion, which may cut down through the three upper bands and leave only a foot of the bed. Normally the following divisions may be made out (Jackson, 1922 and 1926), but the bed is very variable.

Inches.

[Down Cliff Clay with *Dumortieria* above.]

4. The *striatulum* layer (Upper Lias, Yeovilian). Hard grey nodular limestone to soft marl with hard lumps. o— 4

3. The *bifrons* layer (Upper Lias, Whitbian). Hard limestone, mottled pinkish-yellow and red. May contain limestone pebbles and rolled *Hildoceras bifrons*. o—15

2. The *falciferum* layer (Upper Lias, Whitbian). Hard limestone, yellowish-pink, sometimes mottled with red. Sometimes greenish. Fine-grained to conglomeratic. An earthy band with *Pleurotomaria,* and a lenticle of clay, may occur below. 6— 9

1. The *spinatum* layer or Marlstone (Middle Lias, Domerian). Brown, oolitic above, with many fossils, including *Rhynchonella serrata.* Conglomeratic below, with irregular concretionary base. 6—18

The Junction Bed, 3 feet.

[Thorncombe Sands below, with *Rhynchonella thorncombiensis* in a hard band near the top.]

The blue sandy **Down Cliff Clays** above the Junction Bed, 70 feet thick, are inaccessible, and their precise age is not known. They are seen at the top of Down Cliff, but in Thorncombe Beacon they are surmounted by 100 feet of Bridport Sand and a capping of Upper Greensand.

From Eype Mouth to Seatown a good path runs along the cliff-top and a little north of Thorncombe Beacon and Doghouse Hill. The view from these summits is very fine.

EYPE MOUTH TO WEST BAY OR BRIDPORT HARBOUR

(1 mile. Six-inch map, Dorset, 38 S.W.)

This stretch of cliff is the West Cliff of Bridport people. It is also called Watton Cliff, after a neighbouring farm. At first the beds exposed are the same as on the west side of Eype Mouth, but the cliff soon begins to recede from the shore-line and forms a re-entrant angle, within which are slipped masses of clay and limestone. At the angle, which is a quarter of a mile east of Eype Mouth, and affords a way, steep in places, to the cliff-top, a **fault** is well exposed. It runs east and west, nearly in the line of the cliffs, and it lets down Fuller's Earth and Forest Marble against Middle and Upper Lias. The downthrow must be about 500 feet to the south.

On climbing up to the highest terrace in the fault-corner, one sees the five-foot limestone of the Junction Bed forming a conspicuous band in the cliff to the westward. Above it are grey sandy clays, with hard beds at intervals, the Down Cliff Clays. Below it are the yellow Thorncombe Sands, 40 feet thick, with the *Margaritatus* Stone and the Down Cliff Sands below them.

The most interesting of these is the **Junction Bed.** It differs in many respects from the Junction Bed in the western cliffs (p. 31). In the first place it is no longer a junction bed of the Middle and Upper Lias, for the Marlstone is missing. Buckman preferred to call it the Watton Bed in this cliff. The Upper Liassic part of the bed has overstepped not only the Marlstone but also part of the Thorncombe Sands; it is only 40 feet above the *Margaritatus* Stone, whereas the interval is 68 feet at Thorncombe Beacon and 92 feet in Down Cliff. This Upper Lias transgression was attributed by Buckman (1922) to an early movement along the line of the Weymouth anticline.

The Junction Bed has increased in thickness from three to over five feet, and layers of white lithographic limestone appear in it. The fossils also differ widely from those found in it in the western cliffs. The *spinatum* layer is cut out, as has been said, and the lowest horizon is described by Jackson (1926) as pre-*exaratum* (?). Ammonites of *striatulum* type are abundant, but appear to be derived, while *Hammatoceras* and *Dumortieria* indicate higher horizons than are known in the Junction Bed of the western cliffs. With the latter ammonites occur many rolled specimens of *Rhynchonella thorncombiensis*, apparently derived from the eroded Thorncombe Sands.

The Junction Bed presents many extraordinary phenomena. One puzzling feature was the apparent inversion of faunas in one of the blocks examined, *Harpoceras* occurring above *Hildoceras* aff. *bifrons,* with *Grammoceras* of *striatulum* type below. This reversal of the true sequence was attributed by Buckman in 1922 to erosion and redeposition of the highest of the original deposits, containing *striatulum* forms. The underlying deposits with *bifrons* were then exposed to denudation, followed by those with *falciferum,* which were thus redeposited on top of the others. A simpler explanation was afterwards forthcoming; Jackson in 1926 showed that the block in question had turned upside-down in its descent.

The fault face is exposed where it cuts the Junction Bed, which there shows a ferruginous and calcareous coating deposited by solutions percolating along the fault plane.

On the other side of the fault corner, where the cliff trends southward, the downthrown beds at first dip away from the fault, as is often the case, but they soon become nearly horizontal. Bands of shelly limestone separated by clay, seen at the top of the cliff, are part of the **Forest Marble.** They were formerly capped by a tiny patch of Cornbrash, which has disappeared with the recession of the coast. The Forest Marble includes also about 30 feet of grey clay, down to a band containing abundant *Rhynchonella* (*Goniorhynchia*) *boueti.* The very similar grey clays below this band are classed with the **Fuller's Earth** in a purely stratigraphical sense, for none of it has the properties of commercial fuller's earth. *Ostrea acuminata* is found about the middle of the clays. There is no Fuller's Earth Rock, but hard bands containing brachiopods occur at intervals.

Some 500 yards E.S.E. of the fault corner, the clays of the Fuller's Earth assume a nearly vertical attitude, but again flatten out. This is due to another fault, with a downthrow of about 120 feet to the north. *Ostrea acuminata* occurs again here, but the Forest Marble has been removed on the upthrow side of the fault.

A third fault cuts the cliff obliquely just before the West Bay promenade is reached. It also has a downthrow to the north, of about 150 feet, and throws lower beds of the Fuller's Earth against Bridport Sand. Thus the main part of the West Cliff has been let down by trough-faulting. This third fault is more conspicuous than the other two by reason of the colour contrast between the grey Fuller's Earth and the yellow Bridport Sand; but the cutting back of the cliff has rendered it less clear than it was in 1912 when the photograph reproduced in *Plate* III. B was taken. In time the small wedge of Bridport Sand between the W.-E. fault and the W.N.W.-E.S.E. coast will disappear altogether.

The line of the fault may be traced westward across the beach, the indurated Bridport Sand standing out above the shingle. It will be noticed that the Inferior Oolite, which normally comes between the Bridport Sand and the Fuller's Earth, has been cut out of the cliff section by the fault. It appears, however, in the Black Rocks, which are uncovered at low tide to the south of the exposure of Bridport Sand in the foreshore.

There is a path close to the top of this stretch of cliff, with a possible way down at the fault corner. For Bridport, one may either take a bus from the Harbour or walk along the footpath on the western side of the alluvial flat of the River Brit.

BRIDPORT HARBOUR (WEST BAY) TO BURTON BRADSTOCK.

(2 miles. Six-inch maps, Dorset 38 S.W., 45 N.W., 45 N.E.)

The modern name of West Bay for Bridport Harbour is a bad one. There is no bay here, and the name has long been applied to the bay immediately west of Portland.

There is an accumulation of small **shingle** on the east side of the harbour, held up by the jetties that keep the entrance to the harbour clear. On the west side the shingle tends to be swept away without any replenishment from the east, and groynes have been constructed with the object of conserving the shingle and protecting the esplanade.

The shingle represents the end of the Chesil Beach, and the westward travel of beach material at this point is obvious. This is an exception to the usual west-to-east movement along the south coast, so clearly indicated by the bars at the mouths of the Exe, the Otter and the Axe. The southerly component in the trend of the coast probably accounts for this. All along the south coast it is the waves driven by the south-westerly gales that are the principal agents of transport. Here, waves from the S.S.W. have a considerable fetch and tend to move the shingle to the north-west. They are more effective than those from the W.S.W., which would have a contrary effect but have only the fetch of Lyme Bay. The tidal current is a minor factor, but this also runs north-westward here owing to a backwash from the Isle of Portland.

The **East Cliff**, although barely a quarter the height of Golden Cap, is impressive by reason of its sheer face and its steep end toward the Harbour. It is formed of **Bridport Sand** capped by Inferior Oolite.

Between the clays of the Upper Lias and the limestones of the Inferior Oolite is intercalated a yellow sandy deposit which stretches from Gloucestershire to Dorset. In the northern part of its outcrop it is known as the Cotteswold Sands, in the Bath district as the Midford Sands, and farther south as the Yeovil and Bridport Sands. Throughout its 90 miles of outcrop the sand is remarkably uniform, both in its unusually fine grade (90 *per cent.* of it being under 0.1 mm. in diameter) and in its mineral contents, as described by Boswell in 1924; and it was a perfectly natural conclusion that the deposit was all of the same age. However, the ammonites found below, in, and above the sands show that the sandy

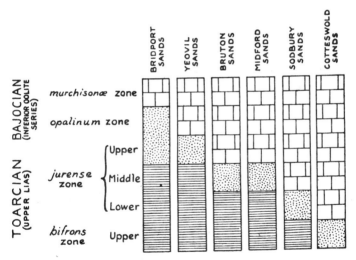

FIG. 9. THE UPPER LIAS-INFERIOR OOLITE SANDS.
Brick pattern represents limestone (Inferior Oolite), dots sand (Upper Lias Sand), and lines clay (Upper Lias Clay). The sandy phase is earlier in the north, later in the south.

phase started in the north and moved southward, as a wave of shallowing, so that the deposition of sand had ceased in the Cotteswold region, and limestone-building had commenced there, before clay had begun to give place to sand in South Dorset. This clear instance of stratal boundaries transgressing time-planes, which was demonstrated by Buckman as long ago as 1889, is a warning that lithic similarity alone is no real evidence of contemporaneity.

The top of the Lias lies somewhere about half-way up the face of the East Cliff, but is marked by no change in lithology. The fine yellow sand is indurated at intervals into bands or nodular masses of calcareous sandstone known as sand-burrs. These give it a banded appearance when weathered. The slight inland dip and the capping of Inferior Oolite account for the vertical face of the cliff. Fossils are scarce; a few may be obtained from the hard bands, and the tumbled masses of Inferior Oolite lying on the shore yield many fossils. However, only part of the Inferior Oolite is present in the East Cliff; the full thickness occurs in Burton Cliff.

East Cliff ends at the valley of the River Bride or Bredy, a strike stream flowing westward from Little Bredy to Burton Bradstock. The river cannot usually be forded dryshod; instead of crossing the shingle, therefore, follow the path inland at the foot of the slope, and in the second field turn right toward a bridge, beyond which another path leads to the shore below Burton Cliff.

Burton Cliff is similar to East Cliff, but in its middle part the Bridport Sands are succeeded by the full thickness of the **Inferior Oolite** (only some 12 feet here) and a little of the Fuller's Earth. Some of the fallen masses on the shore show considerable thicknesses of Inferior Oolite, in which the succession of beds may be recognised. The table on page 37 shows the detailed succession, based on the accounts of Buckman (1910) and Richardson (1928).

On the shore below Burton Villas, where a rough path descends from the road to the beach, a peculiar white limestone occurs. It is unlike any other bed in the neighbourhood. It lies in, on, or against Bridport Sand, but it is close to a fault that throws Fuller's Earth and Forest Marble down some 200 feet to a level with the Bridport Sands. It has yielded a *Nautilus* and species of *Garantiana*. Buckman (1910 and 1922) regarded it as part of the Inferior Oolite, in age between the Red Bed and the *Astarte* Bed. He believed it to have been deposited on a plane of erosion cutting through the Red Bed on to the Bridport Sands; later erosion removed this White Bed from the area to the north and north-west before the *Astarte* Bed was laid down, and a third period of erosion removed the higher beds of the Inferior Oolite at this spot before the Fuller's Earth was deposited. Richardson, on the other hand, suggested in 1915 and 1929 that the White Bed

DETAILS OF THE INFERIOR OOLITE, ETC., NEAR BURTON
BRADSTOCK.

Zones.	FULLER'S EARTH.		
		Ft.	Ins.

Oppelia fusca. The lower part of the Fuller's Earth Clay, with 3 or 4 inches of ferruginous marl, the Scroff, at the base; both yielding *Oppelia fusca* and *Perisphinctes.*

INFERIOR OOLITE.

Parkinsonia parkinsoni. THE FIRST BED (quarrymen's method of enumeration, geologically the last bed). Top 6 inches bluish limestone with *Zigzagiceras zigzag, Oppelia* and *Parkinsonia;* the rest yellowish limestone with few fossils. 2 7

THE SECOND BED. Yellowish limestone with much brown earthy matter; ammonites often rotten. Stout *Parkinsoniæ, Terebratula, Rhynchonella,* sponges. 2 6

THE THIRD BED. Hard grey to almost white limestone, with masses of *Terebratula sphæroidalis,* large and well-preserved *Parkinsonia dorsetensis* and *P. parkinsoni, Strigoceras truellei, Nautilus.* 1 10

THE SHELL BED OR *ASTARTE* BED. A brown ferruginous band with *Crassinella (Astarte) obliqua,* flat evolute *Parkinsoniæ,*
Stephanoceras *Garantiana* spp. 0 4
humphriesianum. Impersistent conglomerate.

Otoites sauzei. THE FOURTH BED OR RED BED. Hard, massive grey limestone, top irregular and iron-stained. Limonitic concretions ("snuff-boxes") below. *Stephanoceras,*
Ludwigella *Witchellia, Sonninia.* 2 10
concava and
Ludwigia YELLOW CONGLOMERATE BED. Yellow marl with small pebbles and rolled
murchisonæ. fossils. 0 2
Leioceras
opalinum. BOTTOM BED OR *SCISSUM* BED. Grey sandy limestone with *Tmetoceras scissum.* 1 6

BRIDPORT SANDS.

RUSTY BED. Brown sandy marl. 0 2
Brown sandstone in two layers with opalinoid ammonites. 1 6
Yellow sands with *Serpula tricarinata.* 2 0
Pleydellia Sandstone. 0 8
aalensis or Sands with ammonites of the *aalensis* pattern
lower *opalinum.* in occasional sand-burrs. 0 10
Sand-burrs and sands, with many ammonites. 4 0
Sands and sand-burrs, seen to 15 feet in the Cliff Hill section and to over 100 feet in Burton Cliff.

is merely an infiltration of calcium carbonate into the Bridport Sands in the vicinity of the fault.

The old cliff by the Coastguard Station and Cliff End is in Forest Marble and Fuller's Earth, but it is much degraded as its base is protected by a stretch of shingle, part of the Chesil Beach. Instead of visiting it, take the road uphill from Burton Villas and then down Cliff Hill to Burton Bradstock.

BURTON BRADSTOCK, BOTHENHAMPTON, BRIDPORT.

(5 miles. Six-inch maps, Dorset 45 N.E., 38 S.E. and S.W.)

Leaving the shore at Burton Villas, take the road uphill and then down to the village through the Cliff Hill cutting. Here about 25 feet of the topmost Bridport Sands are seen, overlain by the *scissum* Bed and the Red Bed of the Inferior Oolite.

Burton Bradstock was formerly noted for its quarries in the Inferior Oolite, and the quarryman's cottage at the corner of the road leading eastward displayed an assortment of local ammonites for sale. The last quarry was closed about 1930; it lay in the allotments south of the junction of the roads to Dorchester and Weymouth. A quarry in Forest Marble lies three-quarters of a mile east of the fork, along the Dorchester road, but the Forest Marble may be visited more conveniently at Bothenhampton.

Continue northward through Burton Bradstock, avoiding the Bridport road on the left. Just beyond the last farm, take a bridle-way on the left and follow it northward for a mile or more. It leads over the Fuller's Earth up to the escarpment of the Forest Marble in North Hill, and reaches a road near Bennet's Hill Farm. Half a mile farther north, where the road turns eastward to Shipton Gorge, take another bridleway running westward to Bothenhampton. The hillside to the north of this track is in Bridport Sands, and a spring thrown out by the sands is passed some 400 yards after leaving the road.

The chimneys of the Bridport Brick and Tile Works mark a very fine exposure of the **Kellaways Clay**, the lowest part of the Oxfordian. It is the most westerly exposure of the clay known in England. Many ammonites and other fossils occur in it, and there are large septarian concretions with calcite forming the septa and selenite (gypsum) on the outside. Excellent crystals of selenite, both simple and twinned forms, also occur in abundance. They owe their origin to the oxidation of pyrite in the clay and the reaction of the SO_3 produced with calcareous matter to form gypsum.

The road to Bothenhampton follows an important fault running east and west and throwing Forest Marble, Cornbrash and Kellaways Clay down against the lower part of the Bridport Sands, a downthrow of some 500 feet to the south. A pit in the **Bridport Sand** is passed on the right; it is worked for use with the clay in brick-making, to check excessive shrinkage of the bricks.

On reaching Bothenhampton, turn to the left at the point where the modern road, after a detour, rejoins the old straight track, and cross the valley to a quarry in **Forest Marble.** The whole hillside is pitted with old workings in this stone. The principal bed worked, for use as wall stones, is about six feet thick, an oolitic shelly limestone with species of *Cyprina, Lima* and *Pecten, Ostrea sowerbyi,* and fragments of *Apiocrinus parkinsoni.*

Returning to Bothenhampton, turn left through the village and continue till the road joins South Street, Bridport; or take a short cut across the fields on the right beyond the railway.

THE BRIDPORT DISTRICT.

Bridport stands on **Middle Lias,** and the hills around it are of **Bridport Sand.** This, with its hard bands or " sand-burrs," may be seen in the East Cliff and in many sunken lane sections; but the Thorncombe Sand of the Middle Lias may look very like it, and the two sands must be distinguished with care.

The conical Colmers Hill, near Symondsbury, Watton Hill and Coneygar Hill, near Bridport Station, show nothing higher than Bridport Sand; but there is a protective capping of **Inferior Oolite** on the top of Chideock Quarry Hill, Allington Hill, and some others. Eastward, the main outcrop of the Inferior Oolite, faulted and dissected, runs from Shipton Gorge past Matravers, Loders, Nettlecombe, Poorton, Mapperton and Beaminster, with Fuller's Earth to the east of it.

The Bothenhampton valley marks a big E.-W. fault which throws down **Forest Marble, Cornbrash** and **Kellaways Clay** against slopes of Bridport Sand on the north. Another E.-W. fault complicates the Forest Marble escarpment in North Hill, while Burton Bradstock lies beyond a valley eroded in the Fuller's Earth and is mainly on the dip-slope of the

Inferior Oolite. The River Bride flows through Bridport Sand from Burton Bradstock to the sea.

Upper Greensand caps most of the hills that reach four or five hundred feet above sea-level, and from Allington Hill or Chideock Quarry Hill a good idea of the 'Cretaceous over-step** may be obtained. At Thorncombe Beacon and Eype Downs the Cretaceous Beds overlie Bridport Sand, but they rest directly on the Middle Lias farther west, at Golden Cap and Langdon Hill, Stonebarrow, Chardown and Hardown Hills, Coppet Hill, Conegar Hill and Lambert's Castle. North of the broad Vale of Marshwood, cut in Lower and Middle Lias, the straight-topped Pilsden Pen attains a height of 900 feet above sea-level. Here too the Cretaceous rests on Middle Lias, but the wooded Lewesden Hill to the east of it is based on Bridport or Yeovil Sand. The downs above Beaminster and Toller Porcorum have Fuller's Earth Clay at their foot; so also have Eggardon Hill and the artificially scarped Shipton Hill, east of Bridport. Still farther east may be seen the Hardy monument on Black Down, above Portisham, where Portland and Purbeck Beds are present beneath the Cretaceous.

Bridport is a good centre, not only for the coastal sections of West Dorset but also for the study of the Dorset type of the Inferior Oolite, with its abundant ammonites, its varied lithology and palæontology, and its apparent non-sequences. The western outlier, on **Quarry Hill, Chideock,** is unfortunately no longer worked. The stone here is 26 feet thick, according to Buckman (1910), and is overlain by the Scroff and the basal Fuller's Earth. The " Limestone Beds " of the workmen (i.e., stone fit to burn for lime), 14 feet thick, are in the *parkinsoni* zone and correspond to the top beds at Burton Bradstock. There is no *Astarte* Bed, and the Red Bed (6 feet, *sauzei* zone) is separated by the 3-foot Wild Bed (*murchisonæ* zone) from the sandy *opalinum* limestone below.

A number of small quarries, many of them disused, occur along the outcrop of the Inferior Oolite indicated above. The best are near **Beaminster,** six miles north of Bridport. The quarry at Horn Park, a mile and a half out of Beaminster on the Broadwindsor road, is particularly rich in ammonites and other fossils, and another good section lies to the south-west of it on the top of Waddon Hill (Stoke Knapp), the difference in level of 300 feet between the two quarries being due to a couple of faults.

From Bridport, too, Abbotsbury may be visited (p. 48), passing quarries in the Forest Marble by the roadside a mile beyond Swyre.

III.—CENTRAL SECTION

In this section*, which may be taken as extending from Abbotsbury to Ringstead Bay and White Nothe, with Weymouth as a convenient centre, the Bathonian Stage of the Middle Jurassic is the lowest deposit to crop out. Clays of the upper part of the **Fuller's Earth** are exposed on the shore of the Fleet south of Langton Herring. No Fuller's Earth Rock is seen, nor is there any of the commercial fuller's earth that occurs near Bath. An oyster bed, ten feet thick, with tightly packed shells of *Ostrea sowerbyi*, mostly of the variety *elongata*, is the most striking feature of the deposit.

The **Forest Marble** consists of bands of limestone made up of broken shells of *Ostrea*, *Pecten*, etc., separated by seams of clay. A band rich in *Rhynchonella* (*Goniorhynchia*) *boueti* and other brachiopods marks the base.

The **Cornbrash** consists of thirty feet of impure limestone and marl. The greater part of it belongs to the Upper Cornbrash and yields *Macrocephalites* and a fauna that has been regarded as Callovian rather than Bathonian. The presence of Lower Cornbrash is only indicated by brachiopods, such as *Terebratula* (*Ornithella*) *obovata* and *T.* (*Cererithyris*) *intermedia*.

The **Oxford Clay** is about 500 feet thick, including the Kellaways Clay (Callovian) below. It marks an extension and deepening of the sea and a return to pyritic blue mud conditions, as in the Lias. The fauna, too, once more shows an abundance of ammonites and belemnites.

In **Corallian** times there was a reversion to shallow-water conditions, and sands and limestones were deposited, including an excellent example of oolitic structure in the Osmington Oolite. Oolite grains are formed to-day in warm, shallow seas, where calcium carbonate is precipitated in concentric layers about a nucleus, constant movement accounting for the spheroidal shape. Some of the grains in the Corallian are large enough to be described as pisoliths (=pea-stones) rather than ooliths (=egg-stones, roe-stones). The fauna is

---

* Sheets 341 and 342 of the Geological Survey's one-inch map are available. They may be cut into sections and mounted as one map, omitting superfluous areas of sea.

TABLE OF STRATA IN THE WEYMOUTH DISTRICT

	RECENT AND PLEISTOCENE	Shingle, Blown Sand, Alluvium, Valley Gravel, Raised Beach, Plateau Gravel, Clay-with-flints and Angular Flint Gravel. (Unconformity)	
	EOCENE	feet Bagshot Beds 300 London Clay 150 Reading Beds 100 (Unconformity)	
UPPER CRETACEOUS	**SENONIAN**	Upper Chalk 900	ZONES *Belemnitella mucronata* *Actinocamax quadratus* *Marsupites testudinarius* *Micraster cor-anguinum* *Micraster cor-testudinarium* *Holaster planus*
	TURONIAN	Middle Chalk 100	*Terebratulina gracilis* *Rhynchonella cuvieri*
	CENOMANIAN	Lower Chalk and Chloritic Marl 100	*Holaster subglobosus* *Schlœnbachia varians*
LOWER CRETACEOUS	**ALBIAN**	Upper Greensand and Gault 150 (Unconformity)	*Stoliczkaia dispar* *Hysteroceras varicosum* *Euhoplites lautus* *Hoplites dentatus*
	NEOCOMIAN	Wealden Beds 1000	(Freshwater deposits)
UPPER JURASSIC	**PURBECKIAN**	Upper Purbeck 50 Middle Purbeck 50 Lower Purbeck 100	(Mainly freshwater deposits)
	PORTLANDIAN	Portland Stone 100 Portland Sand 120	*Titanites giganteus* *Kerberites pseudogigas* *Crendonites gorei*
	KIMMERIDGIAN	Kimmeridge Clay 800	*Pavlovia rotunda* *Pectinatites pectinatus* *Subplanites* *Gravesia gigas* *Aulacostephanus pseudomutabilis* *Pararasenia mutabilis* *Rasenia cymodoce* *Pictonia baylei*
	ARGOVIAN	Corallian 200	*Ringsteadia anglica* *Perisphinctes martelli* *Cardioceras cordatum*
	DIVESIAN	Oxford Clay 500	*Cardioceras præcordatum* and *Greniceras renggeri* *Quenstedioceras lamberti* *Peltoceras athleta* and *Kosmoceras duncani* *Erymnoceras reginaldi* *Kosmoceras jason*
	CALLOVIAN	including "Kellaways Rock" and Kellaways Clay	*Sigaloceras calloviense* *Proplanulites kœnigi*
MID. JURASSIC	**BATHONIAN**	Upper Cornbrash Lower Cornbrash } 30 Forest Marble 80 Fuller's Earth 150	*Macrocephalites macrocephalus* *Clydoniceras discus*

rich in lamellibranchs and echinoids, but corals are scarce in Dorset, except in the topmost few inches.

The **Kimmeridge** Clay is another deposit formed in comparatively deep water. Its thickness is 800 or 900 feet. At Abbotsbury an oolitic iron ore occurs at the base, very like that at the top of the Corallian which has been worked at Westbury in Wiltshire. *Rhynchonella inconstans* and *Ostrea delta* are abundant in the lowest layers; above that ammonites are the chief fossils. Much of the Kimmeridge Clay is bituminous, especially the Kimmeridge " coal " or oil shale, through masses of organic matter having decayed under anaerobic conditions.

Again shallowing set in, and a large part of England became land. The **Portland Sand and Portland Stone** were formed in clear, shallow water. Much of the latter is oolitic, and nodules of chert occur in the lower part. In

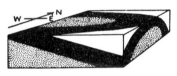

FIG. 10. BLOCK DIAGRAM OF AN ANTICLINE,

with a steep dip to the north and axis pitching to the east.

Purbeck times freshwater limestones and marls were deposited in a delta that was occasionally inundated by the sea, and these conditions persisted into the Cretaceous, the **Wealden Beds** also being of freshwater origin.

The great break that separates the Jurassic and the Cretaceous in West Dorset is here bridged to a large extent. It occurs in the Cretaceous, between the Neocomian and the Albian, only the Aptian (Lower Greensand) being wanting. The Albian is clayey below ("Gault"), sandy and cherty above ("**Upper Greensand** ").

The **Chalk** follows, but only at White Nothe does it reach the coast. Outliers of **Cainozoic** sand cap it at Black Down, north of Portisham, and at Bincombe. The only **Pliocene** deposit known in Dorset is at Dewlish, seven miles north-east of Dorchester, where sand filling a hollow in Chalk yielded bones of Pliocene elephants. The hollow had an artificial appearance, and Osmond Fisher suggested in 1905 that it might have been an elephant trap of human contrivance.

While in West Dorset the beds succeed each other fairly regularly, with an easterly dip, here the strike is east and west and the beds dip north or south. The broad **Weymouth anticline** dominates the area. Its axis runs through Lodmoor, and the southern limb, with a very gentle dip, has suffered greatly from marine erosion, only the Isle of Port-

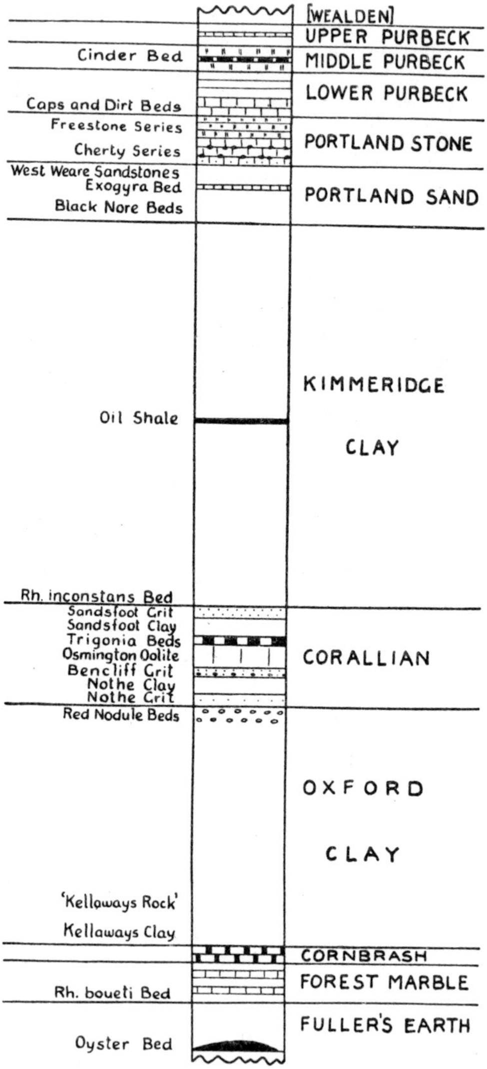

	[WEALDEN]
	UPPER PURBECK
Cinder Bed	MIDDLE PURBECK
Caps and Dirt Beds	LOWER PURBECK
Freestone Series	
Cherty Series	PORTLAND STONE
West Weare Sandstones	
Exogyra Bed	PORTLAND SAND
Black Nore Beds	
Oil Shale	KIMMERIDGE CLAY
Rh. inconstans Bed	
Sandsfoot Grit	
Sandsfoot Clay	
Trigonia Beds	
Osmington Oolite	CORALLIAN
Bencliff Grit	
Nothe Clay	
Nothe Grit	
Red Nodule Beds	
	OXFORD CLAY
'Kelloways Rock'	
Kelloways Clay	
	CORNBRASH
Rh. boueti Bed	FOREST MARBLE
Oyster Bed	FULLER'S EARTH

FIG. 11. THE JURASSIC ROCKS OF CENTRAL DORSET.
Scale: 1 inch to 400 feet.

land and the Weymouth peninsula remaining above sea-level. The northern limb of the anticline dips rather more steeply, giving narrower outcrops, and is much affected by minor flexures and faults, which also trend east and west. The main anticlinal axis pitches to the east, so that the Fuller's Earth, which crops out on the shore of the Fleet, is below sea-level in Weymouth Bay. The Forest Marble, Cornbrash, and Oxford Clay have horseshoe-shaped outcrops, and the Corallian rocks crop out in two separate ridges which are, of course, connected below sea-level eastward.

The Cretaceous Beds, from the Gault upward, are unaffected by these folds and faults, which must therefore be pre-Albian in date. As the Wealden is everywhere conformable with the Purbeckian, they must be post-Neocomian. The only post-Cretaceous disturbances are the Chaldon anticline and its westward continuation in the Ridgeway fault and anticline, and a small syncline at Ringstead. Elsewhere, the Chalk is nearly horizontal, and there is no suggestion of the intense crushing, associated with the Isle of Purbeck overthrust, which affects it only a mile east of White Nothe.

The geological map shows the effect of folds on outcrop with admirable clearness. Thus, the elongated dome south of Poxwell is a perfect little example of a denuded anticline, escarpments of Portland Stone overlooking a central valley in Portland Sands, and the whole forming an inlier of Portlandian in Purbeckian Beds. One mile to the south-west, the V-shaped outcrops of the Portland and Purbeck Beds beneath the transgressive Albian give a clear example of unconformity.

The Chalk and Upper Greensand form the chief reservoir of water, supplying Weymouth from springs at Sutton Poyntz and Portland from wells north of Upwey. There are also copious springs from this source at Portisham and at Spring Bottom, near Ringstead. The Wishing Well at Upwey is a spring at the base of the Portland Stone, and the source of the Wey. The Wey and the Jordon flow southward, and appear to have started on a surface that was not affected by the Weymouth anticline: tributaries come in along the strike of the clays. The Fleet represents the valley of another stream that flowed south-east to join the Wey and enter the sea somewhere east of Portland. Patches of Plateau Gravel and Valley Gravel mark former base-levels of the streams.

Marine erosion in a jointed rock is well shown near Portland Bill, where too a patch of Raised Beach occurs. The Chesil Bank is a grand example of marine deposition, storm

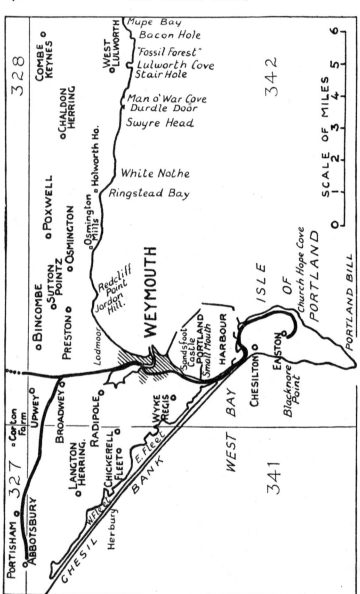

FIG. 12. LOCALITY MAP OF SOUTH CENTRAL DORSET, with sheet boundaries of the Geological Survey maps.

waves having piled up the shingle to a height of forty feet above high-water mark.

EXCURSIONS ROUND WEYMOUTH

The following are suggestions for a week's work, using Weymouth as headquarters. Low tide is advisable for the coast near Weymouth and thence eastward to Ringstead Bay.

FIRST DAY. ABBOTSBURY AND THE SHORE OF THE FLEET

By road (or rail) to Abbotsbury, nine miles N.W. See Lower Kimmeridgian iron ore north of the town, and, if desired, visit the Chesil Bank.

Thence by road to Langton Herring, and walk south to the Coastguard Station, where the Oyster Bed in the Fuller's Earth is exposed. Walk along the shore to Herbury, for Forest Marble, and Fleet, for Cornbrash and Oxford Clay. Turn inland to the brickyards in Oxford Clay at Chickerell. Return by road. Walking distance seven miles (pp. 48-51).

SECOND DAY. PORTLAND.

By road or rail to Portland, four miles south. Walk up the escarpment of the Portland Stone and southward along the Weston road, visiting quarries in work and showing the Portland Freestone Series and the Lower Purbecks. Continue southward by the road, or cliff path from Black Nore, to the Bill.

See Raised Beach, and caves and quarries in Portland Stone, in the south-east part of the Isle. Walk north through Southwell and Easton to Chesilton, and examine the end of the Chesil Bank. Walking distance nine miles (pp. 53-57).

THIRD DAY. THE CORALLIAN ON THE SOUTH SIDE OF THE WEYMOUTH ANTICLINE.

Walk from Weymouth Harbour, over the Nothe and along the shore to Sandsfoot Castle and Wyke Regis Halt.

From Wyke Regis take road and path south-west to the shore of the Fleet and walk west, seeing the same beds again. Walking distance six miles (pp. 58-60 and 50).

This may be divided into two half-days, the first part making a good introduction on arriving at Weymouth.

FOURTH DAY. WEYMOUTH TO OSMINGTON MILLS.

Walk or drive along the coast road to the Coastguard Station and walk along the shore below Furzy Cliff, Redcliff Point and Black Head to Osmington Mills, seeing Oxford Clay, Corallian, and Kimmeridge Clay. Return by cliff path, or by road from Osmington. Walking distance nine miles (pp. 60-64).

FIFTH DAY. RINGSTEAD BAY.

By road to Poxwell Circus, five miles north-east. Note anticline in Portland Stone, exposing Portland Sand. Walk south to the cliff at Holworth House, where the Albian unconformity is well seen.

Descend to the shore and walk westward to Osmington Mills, seeing Kimmeridgian and Corallian. Walking distance five miles (pp. 64-66).

SIXTH DAY. LULWORTH.

Although Lulworth is described in the Eastern Section of this book, it can be visited as easily from Weymouth as from Swanage; and the coastal scenery there is too fine to be missed.   By road to Lulworth Cove, fifteen miles east. Walk west by road and path to St. Oswald's Bay, and along the shore to Durdle Door and Durdle Cove. Return by cliff path to Lulworth Cove, walk round it, and along the cliff path eastward to the Fossil Forest and Mupe Bay. Return, and visit Stair Hole. Walking distance six miles (pp. 81-89).

OTHER DAYS.

Chalk enthusiasts may wish to visit White Nothe (pp. 76-80), or Arish Mell (p. 90). The fine earthwork of Maiden Castle is worth a visit; this may be combined with the well and old quarries at Upwey. Quarries in Portland Stone may also be seen at Chalbury Hill, three miles N.N.E of Weymouth.

ABBOTSBURY AND THE SHORE OF THE FLEET

(10 miles.   Six-inch maps, Dorset, 46 S.W. with 52 N.W., 52 N.E., 52 S.E., 53 N.W., 53 S.W.)

Abbotsbury Swannery lies on Alluvium covering the easily-eroded Oxford Clay of the northern limb of the Weymouth anticline.   This dips north beneath the Corallian rocks (*Fig.* 13), the Osmington Oolite forming a marked escarpment in Linton Hill while a ferruginous grit at the top of the series caps a second escarpment.   The railway is on Kimmeridge Clay.   About the line of the railway and the village street the dip reverses, forming a minor syncline.   The beds are cut off by a fault that runs a little south of west and throws down the Corallian against Forest Marble, and against Fuller's Earth farther to the west.   Upper Greensand and Chalk, capped by Plateau Gravel, form the hills to the north; they are unaffected by fold or fault (which must therefore be pre-Cretaceous or at least pre-Albian), and great masses of them have slipped downhill over the Jurassic clays.

The **Abbotsbury Iron Ore** is best seen in the lane below the west end of Jubilee Coppice, north of the village. The lane, known as Blind Lane, starts a few yards east of the school and runs up over the downs to Gorwell Gate.   In the bottom and sides of the lane, before the wood is reached, is about 20 feet of crumbling reddish-brown rock full of shining pellets of hydrated ferric oxide, with some quartz sand.   Thin seams of concretionary iron oxide occur, and hollow casts of

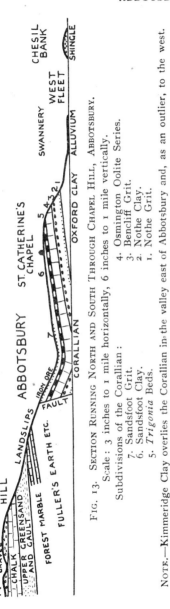

FIG. 13. SECTION RUNNING NORTH AND SOUTH THROUGH CHAPEL HILL, ABBOTSBURY.

Scale: 3 inches to 1 mile horizontally, 6 inches to 1 mile vertically.

Subdivisions of the Corallian:

7. Sandsfoot Grit.
6. Sandsfoot Clay.
5. *Trigonia* Beds.
4. Osmington Oolite Series.
3. Bencliff Grit.
2. Nothe Clay.
1. Nothe Grit.

NOTE.—Kimmeridge Clay overlies the Corallian in the valley east of Abbotsbury and, as an outlier, to the west.

fossils are common. The ore probably averages over 30 per cent. of metallic iron, but it has never been seriously worked. It closely resembles the Upper Corallian ore that has been worked at Westbury in Wiltshire, but is later in date, the ammonites indicating the *Rasenia* zones of the Kimmeridgian. Brachiopods such as *Rhynchonella corallina, R. inconstans,* and *Ornithella lampas* occur in the iron ore.

Just above the Jubilee Coppice the lane crosses the fault and becomes very wet with water escaping from the Upper Greensand over the clays of the Forest Marble. The ascent continues over slipped masses of Upper Greensand, and a small chalk pit may be seen, 300 feet higher than the Jubilee Coppice.

On returning to Abbotsbury, the remains of the Abbey and St. Catherine's Chapel may be visited, the latter giving a good view of the Chesil Bank, the Fleet and Portland. At Shipmoor Point, across the Swannery, Cornbrash is exposed. Beyond that come Forest Marble and Cornbrash, repeated by strike faults, but the beds are better seen in the southern limb of the Weymouth anticline.

It is therefore better to go direct to Langton Herring **and** follow the track southward from Lower Farm, at the west end of the village. Below the Coastguard Station the low cliff shows a mass of oyster shells in the **Upper Fuller's Earth Clay.** The species have long been known as *Ostrea acuminata* and *O. sowerbyi,* but Arkell (1933) identifies the commoner form as *Ostrea sowerbyi* var. *elongata* and states that the true *O. acuminata* marks a constant horizon below the Fuller's Earth Rock and therefore well below the Langton Herring oyster bed.

The Fuller's Earth is the lowest bed exposed in the Weymouth anticline. The beds dip away from it to the north and to the south, and the anticlinal axis itself pitches east, so that where it cuts Weymouth Bay the Oxford Clay is the lowest bed to reach sea-level.

Walking eastward along the shore, we find the oyster bed again at the head of a little bay. The Herbury (or Herbyleigh) peninsula is mainly in **Forest Marble,** the basal band with *Goniorhynchia boueti* being well exposed. This rhynchonellid occurs in the soil of the neighbouring ploughed fields in sufficient abundance to be a guide in mapping. Various species of *Rhynchonella* and *Terebratula* are strewn in numbers on the north shore of Herbury, with slabs of the shelly limestone from the Forest Marble. Ossicles of *Apiocrinus* have been found here, but they are rare.

Forest Marble continues in the low cliffs to beyond Fleet House, and then disappears beneath rubbly, nodular and earthy limestones of the **Cornbrash.** The large *Pholadomya deltoidea, Pleuromya,* and other fossils are abundant on the shore below. The Cornbrash, though comparatively soft and only 30 feet thick, forms a small escarpment between the Forest Marble below and the Oxford Clay above, as may be seen in Fleet Common, at Chickerell, and at Radipole. Old workings at these localities are now grassed over. Two small faults cut the coast at East Fleet.

The **Oxford Clay** is faulted against the Cornbrash and Forest Marble here, and its base is not seen. All the exposures on the shore of the Fleet are poor. The lower beds, with septaria and a few fossils, are seen on the shore south of East Fleet. At Tidmoor Point, behind the rifle range, the low cliff shows clays of the *lamberti* zone, with selenite and numerous fossils. The highest beds appear below the Nothe Grit west of Wyke Regis, followed by the Corallian sequence and finally by Kimmeridge Clay. The Corallian is better studied on the east side of the peninsula (pp. 58-60).

One may well omit this unattractive bit of coast, turning inland at East Fleet and visiting one or both of the large brickyards at Chickerell, the chimneys of which will be noticed. Both are in the lower part of the Oxfordian. The one on the west, half a mile south of Chickerell Church, is mainly in the *duncani* zone, with large flattened concretions, of which the lower ones yield *Erymnoceras reginaldi* and *E. coronatum* (*reginaldi* zone). The more easterly brickyard shows lower beds still. At the top is the sandy equivalent of the Kellaways Rock, with abundant *Gryphæa bilobata;* and the Kellaways Clay below yields species of *Proplanulites* and *Cadoceras*.

THE CHESIL BANK.

The Chesil Bank (Old English *ceosol, cisel* = shingle, *cf.* Chislehurst) stretches 18 miles from Bridport Harbour to Chesilton (Chiswell) Bay in the Isle of Portland. Its width is 170 yards at Abbotsbury, 200 yards at Portland, while its height is 22 feet 9 inches above High Water Mark at the former place and 42 feet 9 inches at the latter, where it forms a magnificent example of a storm-beach. These measurements are given by Sir John Coode (1853), who also states that on the seaward side the shingle extends to a depth below low-water mark of 6 fathoms at Abbotsbury and 8 fathoms at Portland. On the landward side, however, the shingle rests on a bed of clay 3 or 4 feet below low-water mark. The pebbles are well graded, coarsest near Chesilton and diminishing in size toward Bridport, and it is said that fishermen landing on the Bank at night can judge their position by the size of the pebbles.

From Bridport Harbour to Cliff End, the shingle is piled against the cliff. A hollow appears on its landward side at Burton Mere and near Abbotsbury Coastguard Station, and for the eight miles from Abbotsbury to Small Mouth it is separated from the mainland by the shallow lagoon of the Fleet. The western end of the Fleet is brackish and almost tideless, the consolidated shingle being practically water-tight up to ordinary High Water Mark. In the East Fleet, however, wide stretches of mud appear as the tide ebbs through Small Mouth.

The north-eastern shore of the Fleet has clearly never met the full force of the waves, which would cut such soft materials back in a continuous curve. It shows the form of a river valley like that of the Wey, and represents the left bank of a drowned valley. The Fleet is widest, up to half a mile or more, on the Oxford Clay and Fuller's Earth, narrowing to two hundred yards where the shore is of Forest Marble or Cornbrash.

The pebbles of the Chesil Bank are mainly flint and chert, derived from Cretaceous rocks, perhaps by way of Cainozoic gravels such as those at Blackdown and Bincombe. Limestone and chert from the Portland Beds are also common, especially at the eastern end, and another striking constituent is the discoidal pebbles of quartzite, red, purple or white, such as occur in the Bunter pebble beds at Budleigh Salterton in Devon. Much rarer are pebbles of porphyry of a type that can be matched in the Permian breccia of Dawlish. Various tourmalinized rocks, red and black chert, vein quartz, etc., have been identified with the Palæozoic rocks of Cornwall; many of them may have come, like the flints, out of Cainozoic gravels.

The first and simplest explanation of this assemblage of pebbles was that they had been swept by the waves along the shore from west to east, the usual direction on the south coast, and that the larger pebbles had travelled faster than the smaller ones. Then it was suggested that the Bunter pebbles, for example, had been swept *across* Lyme Bay, either from the Budleigh cliffs or from a submerged outcrop; that they had been diverted at Portland and carried by the waves northwestward along the shore, suffering attrition on the way. It was Prestwich in 1875 who first pointed out that the Raised Beach at Portland Bill contained these pebbles, which had therefore come into the district in Pleistocene times, when conditions were very different from those of the present day. Baden-Powell states (1930) that the Raised Beach marks the earliest known date at which pebbles from the Dawlish breccia, from the Budleigh Salterton pebble beds, and perhaps from the Cainozoic gravels, were assembled in one deposit in the Portland district. The Raised Beach is only the remnant of a much larger deposit, formed when the Portland and Purbeck rocks stretched far to the west and east of what is now Portland Bill. North of the extended Portlandian escarpment the Fleet river deposited gravels, remains of which are seen at Fleet Common, at Langton Herring, and near Wyke Regis. It is from the sweeping together of the materials of these ancient shingles and gravels that the Chesil Bank was formed.

At present the beach is practically stationary. The pebbles drift sometimes eastward, sometimes westward, as the storm-winds blow from W.S.W. or S.S.W. There seems to be a general movement toward a point near Chesilton, where the bulk of the beach is greatest and the pebbles are largest. These large pebbles can only be moved by large waves, while smaller stones may travel before smaller waves; this may have a sorting effect. There is a tendency for the beach to be rolled over on itself, and so to retreat toward the north-east, and this movement is most marked at the Portland end. Near Chesilton the beach appears to have overwhelmed blown sand.

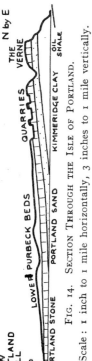

FIG. 14. SECTION THROUGH THE ISLE OF PORTLAND.
Scale: 1 inch to 1 mile horizontally, 3 inches to 1 mile vertically.

A smaller beach, the Portland Beach, stretches from the northern end of the Isle of Portland toward Weymouth, ending at Small Mouth. It is formed of limestone and chert of purely local origin. This also is now stationary, being protected by the Portland Breakwater.

THE ISLE OF PORTLAND

(Periphery 9½ miles. Six-inch maps, Dorset 58 N.E., 58 S.E., 60 N.E.)

The Isle of Portland, four miles long by a mile and two-thirds in greatest width, is tied to the mainland by ten miles of the Chesil Bank. Road and railway connection is by way of Wyke Regis and the Portland Beach, with bridges across Small Mouth. At the northern end, where the Verne forti-fications cap the escarpment of Portland Stone and Sand resting on Kimmeridge Clay, the elevation is 495 feet. At Portland Bill it falls to about 30 feet. The interven-ing area is essentially the dip-slope of the Portland Stone, with a capping of Lower Purbeck, greatly cut up by quarrying in the northern part. The dip is about 1½°, a little east of south.

Kimmeridge Clay forms the lower northern slope and stretches in narrow strips beneath the cliffs as far as Black Nore on the west and Church Hope Cove on the east, where it sinks below sea-level. At Castletown the Kimmeridge Coal (Oil Shale) was formerly seen between tide marks. Nowhere is there a good section, the outcrop being covered with waste tipped from the quarries above and with the debris of landslips. As the sea attacks the clay, the foundations yield beneath the crags of Portland Stone and great slices of cliff break away, yielding masses of rock which may serve as breakwaters and so protect the coast for a time.

The **Portland Sand** is not very well exposed. The clearest section is in West Weare Cliff, between Chesilton and Black Nore, but the Portland Clay, at the top of the series, occurs only below the Verne Fort. The local subdivisions are as follows, according to Arkell :—

	feet.
[Portland Stone, Cherty Series, above.]	
Portland Clay (seen in N. end of island only)	0—14
West · Weare Sandstones	30—40
Exogyra Bed	8
Upper Black Nore Beds	35
Black Nore Sandstone	6
Lower Black Nore Beds	seen to 40
[Kimmeridge Clay below.]	
	Total about 140

Of these, the *Exogyra* Bed is the most conspicuous. It is a stiff marl closely packed with *Exogyra nana,* and it weathers out as a prominent massive band. The boundary between Kimmeridge Clay and Portland Sand is obscure.

The lower part of the **Portland Stone** is full of chert and useless for building. There is a basal shell bed, about 8 feet of hard crystalline limestone, full of shells which can only be extracted when they have weathered out. This is followed by 60 or 70 feet of limestones with chert nodules. In places the rock is full of hollow casts of fossils, *Trigonia incurva* and *Protocardia dissimilis,* while *Serpula gordialis* sometimes abounds. Large Behemothan ammonites also occur.

The **Freestone Series** of the Portland Stone has been used for local buildings since Norman times. Rufus Castle was built of it about 1080, Portland Castle and Sandsfoot Castle in the reign of Henry VIII. It was Inigo Jones, chief architect and surveyor-general to James I., who first brought it to London and used it in the Banqueting Hall in Whitehall (1619) and for repairing Old St. Paul's. After the Great Fire of 1666 Sir Christopher Wren used immense quantities in re-building St. Paul's Cathedral and other churches, and for the Monument and Old Temple Bar. Other notable examples of Portland Stone in London are the Mansion House, British Museum and Somerset House (all Eighteenth Century), the Foreign Office and neighbouring buildings, the Imperial Institute, the Victoria and Albert Museum, and the County Hall.

Portland Stone can be obtained in large blocks; it is a " free " stone, having the same properties in all directions; it is very suitable for carvings and mouldings; and if properly selected and seasoned it is very durable, even in a smoke-polluted atmosphere. In towns, a dark incrustation of calcium sulphate mixed with soot forms beneath cornices and in other sheltered nooks, contrasting with the white rain-swept areas and giving a pleasing effect of age. Portland cement is an indirect testimony to the esteem in which Portland Stone is held: it was never made at Portland, but it resembles Portland Stone, or so the manufacturers wished to imply.

The Freestone Series at Portland is about 25 feet thick. The divisions are as follows:—

	[Purbeck Beds above.]	feet.
Roach		about 3
Whit Bed		7
Curf and Chert		0— 6
Base Bed Roach		0— 3
Base Bed		10
	[Cherty Series below.]	

The **Base Bed,** sometimes called the Best Bed, is a fine white oolitic limestone of uniform texture and specially suitable for fine carvings and indoor work. It may be capped by the Little Roach or Base Bed Roach, which contains hollow casts of *Trigonia* and other shells. The Curf and Chert (or Flinty) Bed marks a return to the conditions under which the Cherty Series was accumulated.

The **Whit Bed** is a buff-coloured limestone, oolitic, but with much shell-debris. It is harder and more durable than the Base Bed, but less uniform, shell fragments and calcite veins (" snail creeps ") tending to weather up and spoil the effect if the stone is used for fine carvings. It may be used successfully for bolder carvings, and is the best stone for general building purposes. Current-bedding is sometimes seen, as in the piers of the railings surrounding the Natural History Museum at South Kensington. The gigantic ammonites of Portland are confined to the Curf and the Whit Bed.

The **Roach** is a tough oolite, full of hollows where shells have been dissolved away. The commonest species are *Trigonia gibbosa* and *Cerithium* (*Aptyxiella*) *portlandicum,* the " horses' heads " and " Portland screws " of the quarrymen. The " screws " are confined to this bed. The Roach is unsuitable for use as an ordinary building stone, but its strength and durability make it an excellent stone for sea walls

and harbour works. Vast quantities were used in the Portland Breakwater, and it may be seen also in the Cobb at Lyme
Regis and in the waterfalls of the Serpentine in London.

Above the Roach, most quarry-sections show some thickness
of the **Lower Purbeck Beds,** and nearly 100 feet are exposed in the cliffs near Southwell. These are mainly limestones of freshwater origin. The quarrymen distinguish the
following divisions :—

							feet.
Top Rubble (Shingle, Slat and clay). Top not seen.							
Bacon Tier and Aish ...	...	...	...	...	...	...	4— 8
Soft Burr	...	...	...	...	...	...	1
Great Dirt Bed	...	...	...	...	...	...	$\frac{1}{4}$— $1\frac{1}{2}$
Top Cap	...	...	...	...	...	...	5—15
Lower Dirt Bed ...	...	...	...	...	...	...	0— $\frac{1}{2}$
Skull Cap	...	...	...	...	...	...	$1\frac{1}{2}$— 5

[Roach below.]

The **Skull Cap** and the **Top Cap** are tufaceous limestones, contrasting in texture with the Roach beneath, but
massive enough to be mistaken for Portland Stone at a distance. The **Dirt Beds** that occur above the Top Cap, and
sometimes also below it, are dark earthy bands with pebbles
of limestone. They represent old soils on which grew cycads
and coniferous trees (*Araucarites*), till they were submerged
beneath the waters of a lagoon that covered them with calcareous tufa. These trees and cycads (" fossil birds' nests "
to the quarrymen) are silicified, and the trunks of the trees
are said to lie mostly in one direction, as though blown down
by a westerly wind. They are found chiefly in the **Soft Burr,**
the tufa forming bosses or burrs above them.

The **Aish** is a soft earthy limestone. Some of the tree-
trunks pass up into it. The **Bacon Tier** is a streaky limestone with bands of sand. The **Top Rubble,** which may be
very thick as compared with the other beds, consists of bands
of thin-bedded limestone separated by clay. The thin limestones are much used locally for walling, and the names Slat
and Shingle suggest their use as a roofing material, as slates
or shingles. In the southern part of the island the beds below
the Aish are absent.

Two sets of joints traverse the Portland Stone and Caps.
The master joints run N.N.E.-S.S.W., and are known as
" gully joints " or "southers." They are often widened to
two feet or more, partly by solution, but more perhaps by
movement over the less stable Portland Sands. The " east-
westers " cut these joints nearly at right angles. The thin-

bedded Purbeck limestones above the caps are not affected by these joints, except in so far as they have sagged and collapsed over the gullies. The walls of the gullies are often coated with stalagmite, and some have yielded bones of Recent mammalia. The joints have governed the form of the cliffs, as well as the methods of quarrying.

The chief problem in quarrying on Portland is the disposal of the worthless overburden, which may be as much as 60 feet thick. The waste from the older quarries was dumped over the cliffs. Now it is usually built up in the worked-out parts of the quarries, which tend to progress in long narrow strips (*Plate* 4B). The Top Rubble is cleared as far as a gully joint, the line of which is indicated by broken and collapsed bedding. The Caps are blasted. The Roach, Whit Bed and Base Bed are quarried in successive tiers, by cutting grooves horizontally and vertically, lining them with steel plates, and driving in wedges which are hammered in till a block separates. It is then lifted out and scappled, or trimmed.

The cliff scenery of the Isle of Portland is magnificent, even in the southern part of the island, where the elevation is slight. After visiting quarries in work, or recently in work, near Easton, one may follow the cliff path down the west coast to Portland Bill, returning along the east cliff, where more quarries have recently been started.

At the Bill, and for a mile north-eastward to Sand Holes, sections in **Raised Beach** will be noticed. This attains a height of 65 feet above Ordnance Datum, and its wave-cut platform in Purbeck and Portland Beds slopes from about 50 feet down to about 20 feet. The Raised Beach consists of shingle passing into sand toward the north-east, and contains shells of mollusca still common in British seas, such as *Littorina, Patella, Purpura, Ostrea* and *Mytilus,* but including northern forms that do not now live south of the Wash or, in some cases, south of Scotland. The Raised Beach is overlain by Head (angular rubble, probably frost-shattered), and rainwash containing land and fresh-water shells. Besides flints, chert and local limestones, the Raised Beach contains small quartz pebbles and a few Budleigh quartzites and Dawlish porphyries (p. 52). Granite boulders have also been recorded. If they were brought by ice, as seems probable, this Raised Beach must be either postglacial or interglacial, for its fauna shows that it is not glacial (see Baden-Powell, 1930).

E

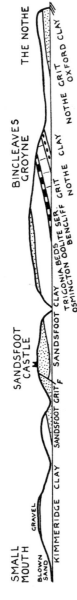

FIG. 15. THE CLIFFS BETWEEN SMALL MOUTH AND WEYMOUTH.

Scale: 3 inches to 1 mile horizontally, 12 inches to 1 mile vertically.

(Length of section, two miles.)

SMALL MOUTH TO WEYMOUTH HARBOUR

(2¼ miles.   Six-inch maps, Dorset, 58 N.W., 53 S.W., 53 S.E.)

The classic sections in the Corallian Beds at Sandsfoot, Bencliff and the Nothe are still worth a visit, though civilisation, as represented by the Portland Breakwater (checking coast erosion), the Bincleaves torpedo works, and the Nothe Gardens, has spoilt a large part of them in recent years. The southern end of the cliffs may be reached by train to Wyke Regis Halt on the line from Melcombe Regis Station to Portland, or by bus to the Wyke Hotel and thence to the footbridge at the Halt.

Blown Sand caps the low cliff of Kimmeridge Clay immediately north of the pier at Small Mouth, and poor sections may be seen in slips. The railway cutting north of the Halt showed pockets of gravel, mostly black chert, on the **Kimmeridge Clay.** The latter dips southward, forming part of the southern limb of the Weymouth anticline. Its upper part, masked by slips and debris of the overlying Portlandian, may be seen across the harbour in the northern end of Portland, and as we follow the coast north-eastward the underlying Corallian rocks soon appear, first in the foreshore and then rising in the cliff.

The **Corallian** here consists of a series of limestones, calcareous sand-stones and clays. The divisions seen here can be recognised in the northern flank of the Weymouth anticline, at Abbotsbury and Osmington, for example. They are as follows :

[Kimmeridge Clay above.]   feet.

Sandsfoot Grit	...	...	...	...	...	...	24
Sandsfoot Clay	...	...	...	...	...	...	38
Trigonia Beds	...	...	...	...	...	...	12
Osmington Oolite Series	...	...	...	...	...	...	45
Bencliff (Bincleave) Grit	...	...	...	...	...	...	35
Nothe Clay	...	...	...	...	...	...	40
Nothe Grit ...	...	...	...	...	...	...	30

[Oxford Clay below.]

The two clays give rise to coves in the coastline and valleys inland, while the grits and limestones form higher ground.

The **Sandsfoot Grit** (to take the beds in the descending order in which we find them in this traverse) first appears on the foreshore near the northern end of the railway embankment. It consists of ferruginous red and brown sands with a blue sandy clay, five feet thick, in the middle. *Ostrea delta* and other fossils occur, as well as markings that have been attributed to fucoids. The top is obscure, but may be better seen in the bank of the Fleet, south of Wyke Regis. Above the sands come 15 feet of clay and 15 inches of ferruginous oolite and clay-ironstone nodules, which Arkell regards as equivalent to the Westbury iron ore beds. These are succeeded by the *Rhynchonella* (*Rhactorhynchia*) *inconstans* Bed of the Kimmeridge Clay.

Sandsfoot Castle, now at the edge of the cliff, shows that there has been considerable coast-erosion since it was built in 1539.

The **Sandsfoot Clay** appears in the cliff below Sandsfoot Castle and forms a small undercliff round Castle Cove. The valley here is also cut in it, the hill to the north being capped by an outlier of Sandsfoot Grit. It is a blue sandy clay containing *Ostrea delta* and *Exogyra nana*.

The **Trigonia .Beds** appear in the Western ·Ledges, where, at low tide, they form a platform with a rugged surface. The limestone is very hard, and it is easier to see the shells of *Trigonia clavellata* to which the name is due than to extract them.

The **Osmington Oolite** Series forms similar ledges, but whiter and with a smoother surface, south of the Portland Breakwater. Part of it shows a beautifully oolitic structure.

The **Bencliff** or **Bincleave Grit** crops out on Admiralty property at the Bincleaves torpedo station, and runs inland along the escarpment overlooking Weymouth. It consists chiefly of brown sandstones with a band of hard sandstone doggers at the base.

The **Nothe Clay** forms the cove north of Bincleaves

and runs up the dip-slope of the Nothe Gardens. It is a blue clay in which *Gryphæa dilatata* and other Oxford Clay fossils mingle with those of the Corallian.

The **Nothe Grit** is seen in the ledges below the Jubilee Walk and it forms the promontory known as the Nothe (*i.e.*, the Nose, Ness, or Naze). Its escarpment drops steeply to the Oxford Clay in which Weymouth Harbour has been eroded. It consists of hard brown grits with fucoid markings, and softer sandy and clayey beds with concretions.

WEYMOUTH
(Six-inch map, Dorset 53)

Weymouth Harbour owes its origin to the soft Oxford Clay, in which Weymouth Bay is eroded, dipping southward beneath the Nothe Grit. Where the dip brings the top of the clay below sea-level, erosion is slowed down and the grit forms the protective promontory of the Nothe. The old town, popularised by George III., is built mainly on a strip of Alluvium between the sea and the Back Water, or Radipole Lake, which limited its growth. The marsh of Lodmoor, where the area of Alluvium on Oxford Clay is liable to floods, has checked its expansion northward. Modern suburbs of Weymouth have sprung up at Radipole, Westham, Rodwell and Wyke Regis.

In recent years the form of Radipole Lake has been modified. Radipole Park Drive was constructed, and the area between this road and the railway was reclaimed by means of a dredger which cut into the Oxford Clay of the lake floor and pumped the debris across the road until the required level was attained. Near the Gas Works, too, former mud flats have been raised to road level, chiefly with chalky Portland Stone from Chalbury Hill, near Preston.

WEYMOUTH TO OSMINGTON MILLS
(4½ miles. Six-inch maps, Dorset 53 S.E., 53 N.E., 54 N.W.)

North of Weymouth Harbour a wide stretch of nearly level sand extends from the Esplanade to Low Water Mark*. Beyond the Jubilee Clock shingle appears, first at the head of

---

* The Present is the key to the Past, and it is worth while to collect and identify the shells that are strewn in great variety over these sands. The lighter and generally whiter streaks, left by the backwash of the receding waves, should be examined with a lens for minute mollusca and foraminifera. If these are seen, a matchboxful may be scraped up and worked over at leisure with a lens, a moistened camel's hair brush, and a little water in a watch glass or other vessel.

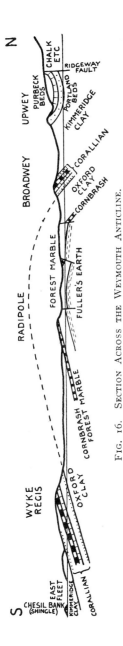

Fig. 16. Section Across the Weymouth Anticline.
Scale : 0.9 inch to 1 mile horizontally, 3 inches to 1 mile vertically.

the beach and then sloping steeply from above High Water Mark to Low.

A low ridge of bare Oxford Clay separates the Weymouth Alluvium from that of Lodmoor. There is no section now, but before the Greenhill Gardens were made Damon recorded a number of fossils from the upper part of the Oxford Clay exposed in a low cliff here. The marshy tract beyond, and the road that skirts it, are protected from the sea by a storm-beach of shingle, retained by groynes at the north-eastern end.

The cliff begins where the road turns inland at the Coastguard Station. It is known as Furzy Cliff, the seaward end of Jordon Hill, which is part of the ridge of Corallian rocks that runs westward to Broadwey and Abbotsbury. The dip is northerly here, for we have crossed the axis of the Weymouth anticline. Note that this axis is not horizontal but pitches eastward; hence the Oxford Clay is the lowest bed to crop out in Weymouth Bay, while Cornbrash and Forest Marble appear near Radipole and Fuller's Earth near Langton Herring. Note also that the outcrops, as shown on the map, are narrower on the north than on the south, indicating a steeper dip in the northern limb of the anticline than in the southern. The northern limb, too, is more affected by minor folds and faults.

Furzy Cliff shows the upper part of the **Oxford Clay**, pale blue-grey in colour, with abundant shells of the large *Gryphæa dilatata* and lines of septarian concretions, or " kidney-stones." These are hard cream-coloured cement-stones (clay with a calcareous bond), red on the outside, with cracks filled with crystalline calcite. Some of them contain casts of *Modiola* and *Astarte*. Thin veins of calcite occur in the clay. Damon recorded a bed with tubes of the worm *Vermilia sulcata* here. The overlying Corallian does not appear in the cliff section.

Furzy Cliff ends at the mouth of the Jordon, a small stream rising at the foot of the Chalk downs a mile and a half inland, and flowing through Sutton Poyntz and Preston. Some good meanders may be seen in its lower course.

Beyond the Jordon's mouth and Bowleaze Cove, **Corallian** rocks form the cliff as far as Redcliff Point (Ham Cliff of the old one-inch map). They are horizontal, or dip very gently northward. The subdivisions are listed on page 65. At the base of the cliff appears the Nothe Grit, and above it the more massive Preston Grit, with *Trigonia hudlestoni* and other fossils. The Nothe Clay forms a small undercliff, backed by Bencliff Grit and the Osmington Oolite Series. Among the fallen blocks strewn on the shore are many great doggers, oval, flattened, up to six feet or more across, of calcareous sandstone, fallen from the Bencliff Grit. The cuboidal blocks are Preston Grit.

At Redcliff Point a fault, running east and west, brings up Oxford Clay with a small cap of Nothe Grit, on the south, to the level of the Osmington Oolite on the north.

Beyond Redcliff Point a minor anticline brings up **Oxford Clay** once more, in the most easterly exposure of this clay on the south coast. The upper beds are as in Furzy Cliff, with *Gryphœa dilatata* and *Modiola bipartita,* but lower beds with small pyritised ammonites are exposed along the axis of the anticline.

The northern limb of this anticline dips steeply, at 50° or more, and the Nothe and Preston Grits rapidly descend from the cliff top to sea level, where they form a reef some thirty yards from the shore. The Nothe Clay comes down to the shore at the Short Lake ravine, and the higher beds of the **Corallian** form the cliff beneath the great slips of Kimmeridge Clay in Black Head.

The Bencliff Grit is still characterised by the huge doggers at its base. The Osmington Oolite Series is 65 feet thick, but only a fraction of this is oolite. The *Trigonia* Beds are some 15 feet of tough reddish limestone crowded with *Trigonia clavellata* and other bivalves. They form a reef parallel to the shore between Black Head and Osmington Mills. The Sandsfoot Clay resembles the Kimmeridge Clay and, like it, contains *Ostrea delta.* The Sandsfoot Grit is

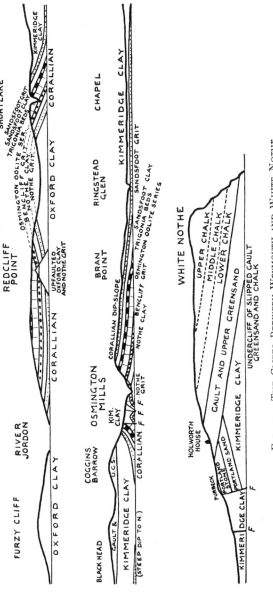

FIG. 17. THE CLIFFS BETWEEN WEYMOUTH AND WHITE NOTHE.

Scale: 3 inches to 1 mile horizontally, 6 inches to 1 mile vertically.

much diminished and is succeeded by the Ringstead Waxy Clay and the Ringstead Coral Bed, a thin clayey limestone containing shells and corals. This can be traced for some distance just above the beach. It marks the top of the Corallian.

The basal part of the **Kimmeridge Clay,** with *Rhynchonella inconstans* and *Ostrea delta,* is seen near the shore below Black Head, and the section extends up to above the Oil Shale horizon in the western part. The dip is northward at about 50°, while the Upper Greensand, dipping gently to the east, truncates successive zones of the Kimmeridgian and rests on the *Rasenia* zones near Osmington Mills. Water from the Upper Greensand causes repeated landslips in the clay; ponds and marshes are held up, and mud-glaciers creep down the cliffs.

The Corallian Beds rise again in the cliff at Osmington Mills. Trough faulting throws them down beneath a wedge of Kimmeridge Clay, but they run out to sea westward in a sharp anticline between the faults, the *Trigonia* Beds forming a reef on either side of the anticlinal axis. Further faulting renders this a very complex little area.

The return to Weymouth may be made by bus from Osmington village. Or the cliff path may be followed past Coggin's Barrow and above the landslips of Black Head, traversing Upper Greensand with two outliers of Lower Chalk. By keeping near the 300-foot contour until the Shortlake drive has been crossed, the escarpment of the Portland Stone and Sand will be seen running westward. Small exposures in the Portland Stone look very like chalk pits, with flints in the chalk*. A good path will be found running past Eweleaze Barn to Redcliff Point and then along the cliff top to Bowleaze Cove and Furzy Clift.

OSMINGTON MILLS AND RINGSTEAD BAY
(2 miles. Six-inch map, Dorset, 54 N.W.)

The cliff at Osmington Mills shows a nearly complete section of the **Corallian Rocks,** the dip-slope of the Sandsfoot Grit forming the top of the cliff. The dip is eastward, and the lower beds are somewhat obscured, but the Nothe and Preston Grits are seen forming the waterfall, with Bencliff

---

* The Portlandian Beds north of Weymouth differ considerably from those of Portland and of Purbeck. The top of the Portland Sand is in places so hard that it makes a strong feature and has been mapped as Portland Stone (Arkell, 1935).

Grit faulted down against them to the north. Eastward, the Nothe Clay gives rise to an undercliff backed by low cliffs of Bencliff Grit and the Osmington Oolite Series. Great doggers of false-bedded calcareous sandstone from the Bencliff Grit may be seen on the foreshore.

CORALLIAN ROCKS IN THE NORTHERN LIMB OF THE
WEYMOUTH ANTICLINE

[Kimmeridge Clay above]

	ft.	in.
Ringstead Coral Bed	0	8
Ringstead Waxy Clay	10	0
Sandsfoot Grit	7	0
Sandsfoot Clay	25	0
Trigonia Beds	20	0
Osmington Oolite Series	60	0
Bencliff Grit	12	0
Nothe Clay	40	0
Preston Grit ... ...:.	6	0
Nothe Grit	27	0

[Oxford Clay below.]

The **Osmington Oolite Series** is 60 feet thick, but only some 6 feet of it is a white oolitic limestone. The remainder consists of grey marls, oolitic or pisolitic, with bands of impure nodular limestone. Near the base is a hard limestone full of shells of *Chlamys qualicosta, C. fibrosa,* and *Exogyra nana,* and two feet above it is a seam of pisolite which Arkell finds to be very constant at this horizon. The Osmington Oolite Series forms most of the cliff at Bran Point and the reef known as Bran Ledge, the curved form of which indicates the nose of an anticline pitching eastward.

The *Trigonia* Beds, bands of hard ironstained limestone full of *Trigonia clavellata* and other fossils, are seen near the cliff top at Bran Point and descend to the shore at Perry Ledge. They also form Ringstead Ledge, opposite the Methodist Chapel, and the reef to the east of it.

The **Sandsfoot Clay** contains *Ostrea delta* in abundance. The **Sandsfoot Grit** is only about 7 feet thick, sandy marls capped by red sandstone. Above it comes the **Ringstead Waxy Clay,** 10 feet of ferruginous clay containing clay-ironstone nodules. The Corallian sequence ends with the **Ringstead Coral Bed**, an eight-inch band of tough argillaceous limestone containing the corals *Thamnastræa* and *Thecosmilia,* and lamellibranchs such as *Ctenostreon proboscideum, Lima,* and *Pecten.* It will be observed that in Dorset the Corallian is hardly worthy of the name. The Coral Bed may be traced at the foot of the cliff, where not hidden by slipped Kimmeridge Clay, for some 500 yards east of the

Methodist Chapel.   The shore follows the strike, the dip being northward.

The low cliff above is in the *Pictonia* and *Rasenia* zones of the **Kimmeridge Clay** capped by flint gravel.   The large oyster, *Ostrea delta,* is abundant, and *Rhynchonella inconstans* occurs with *Pictonia* in the lowest 3½ feet of the clay. This is followed by a six-inch band of marl and limestone full of *Exogyra nana.*   As the cliff increases in height, near the centre of Ringstead Bay, the *Aulacostephanus* zone comes in, and, at a higher level, the Oil Shale or Kimmeridge Coal horizon, but sections are poor.

The cliff west of Holworth House is known as the Burning Cliff, from the " pseudovolcanic phenomena " seen there in 1826, when rapid oxidation of iron pyrites ignited the oil shales.   They smouldered below the surface for about four years, and the overlying shales were baked to the condition of red tiles, or even to a scoriaceous slag, as described by Buckland and De la Beche.

A couple of faults running northward, with downthrows to the east, have the effect of bringing forward the outcrop of the **Portland Sand** and **Stone** from half a mile inland to the brow of the cliff.   A path runs up the cliff by the second fault and shows Portland Sand passing gradually up into the Cherty Series of the Portland Stone.   Bands of oolitic limestone, and of Roach, full of hollow casts of shells, follow, but the rocks here differ markedly from those of Portland on the one side and Purbeck on the other.   Lower Purbeck limestones, with Cyprids and *Cyrena,* cap the section.

The Portland and Purbeck Beds are seen, where cut by the fault, to dip northward at about 25°.   A little farther east, in the cliff below Holworth House, the **Cretaceous Beds,** dipping gently eastward, pass over the upturned edges of the Purbeck Beds, Portland Stone and Portland Sand, on to the Kimmeridge Clay, giving the most striking example of angular discordance to be seen in Dorset.   There is a basal pebble bed, followed by sandy clays (mapped as Gault) and sands, with chert in the upper part.   This Upper Greensand is Albian in age, like the Gault.   Above comes the Chloritic Marl, and then the Chalk, the latter forming the fine cliffs that run out to White Nothe.   Below them is an undercliff with fallen masses of Chalk and Greensand that have slipped over the unstable foundation of Kimmeridge Clay.

The return may be by the cliff path to Osmington Mills, or northward to strike the elongated dome of Poxwell Circus (p. 45).

IV.—EASTERN SECTION

In this section is included not only that part of the " Isle " of Purbeck lying south of the Chalk ridge of the Purbeck Hills, with the Eocene tract about Studland and Poole Harbour, but also the Chalk cliffs westward to White Nothe. Swanage is the only town of any size, and it makes a good centre.*

The **Kimmeridge Clay** is the lowest bed exposed in East Dorset, and of that nothing below the *Aulacostephanus* zone is seen. It is unfortunate that at Kimmeridge, the type locality, the lower limit of the Stage cannot be determined; Ringstead Bay, nine miles westward, is the nearest point where the junction with the Corallian can be seen. In and near Kimmeridge Bay the beds are mainly shales, with strong bands of calcareous stone at intervals. These may be due to secondary segregation of calcareous matter, as in the Blue Lias. The Oil Shale (Kimmeridge Coal, or Blackstone), occurring near the middle, points to organic remains having decomposed under favourable conditions. It has been used locally as a fuel, but it has too much sulphur and is too thin (about 3 feet) to be commercially valuable. Bituminous matter, however, is not confined to this one band. It may be noted that at Heathfield in Sussex the railway station has for many years been lighted by natural gas emanating from the Kimmeridge Clay below.

The change from these comparatively deep-water shales to the sands and limestones of the Portlandian is a gradual one, and neither the base nor the top of the **Portland Sand** is clearly marked. Different writers have adopted different limits. The sands and marls pass up into sandy limestones with chert and so into the **Cherty Series** of the Portland Stone, which is commercially valueless. In the **Freestone Series,** above it, oolite grains, fine calcitic mud and shell fragments were mingled in various proportions, yielding stone that is not inferior to that of Portland. It is said, indeed, to be more resistant to weather, and is distinguished as Purbeck-Portland. Locally, at Tilly Whim, an oyster-bed occurs near the top.

---

* Sheets 342 and 343 of the one-inch map of the Geological Survey cover this area. They may be cut into sections and mounted as one map, omitting superfluous areas of sea.

TABLE OF STRATA IN SOUTH-EAST DORSET

			ZONES
	RECENT AND PLEISTOCENE	Blown Sand, Calcareous Tufa, Peat, Alluvium, Plateau Gravel, Angular Flint Gravel of the Chalk Downs. (Unconformity)	
	OLIGOCENE	Bembridge Limestone etc.	
	EOCENE	feet Bagshot Beds 400 London Clay 250 Reading Beds 100 (Unconformity)	
UPPER CRETACEOUS	SENONIAN	Upper Chalk 1000	ZONES *Belemnitella mucronata* *Actinocamax quadratus* *Marsupites testudinarius* *Micraster cor-anguinum* *Micraster cor-testudinarium* *Holaster planus*
UPPER CRETACEOUS	TURONIAN	Middle Chalk 100	*Terebratulina gracilis* *Rhynchonella cuvieri*
UPPER CRETACEOUS	CENOMANIAN	Lower Chalk and Chloritic Marl 140	*Holaster subglobosus* *Schlœnbachia varians*
LOWER CRETACEOUS	ALBIAN	Upper Greensand and Gault 150 (Usually an unconformity)	*Stoliczkaia dispar* *Hysteroceras varicosum* *Hoplites dentatus*
LOWER CRETACEOUS	APTIAN	Lower Greensand 200	*Deshayesites deshayesi*
LOWER CRETACEOUS	NEOCOMIAN	Wealden 2300	(Freshwater deposits)
UPPER JURASSIC	UPPER PURBECK 60 feet	*Viviparus* Clays Marble Beds *Unio* Beds Broken Shell Limestone	Mainly freshwater deposits,
UPPER JURASSIC	MIDDLE PURBECK 160 feet	Chief Beef Beds *Corbula* Beds Upper Building Stones Cinder Bed Lower Building Stones Mammal Bed	zoned on Ostracods— *Cypridea punctata* (U) *C. granulosa* var. *fasciculata* (M)
UPPER JURASSIC	LOWER PURBECK 170 feet	Marls with Gypsum Broken Beds Caps and Dirt Beds	*Cypris purbeckensis* (L)
UPPER JURASSIC	PORTLAND STONE 100 feet	Shrimp Bed *Titanites* Bed Pond Freestone Chert Vein Listy Bed House Cap Under Picking Cap Under Freestone Cherty limestones and calcareous sandstones	*Titanites giganteus* *Kerberites pseudogigas*
UPPER JURASSIC	PORTLAND SAND 120 feet	The Parallel Bands St. Alban's Head Marls White Cementstone Emmit Hill Marls The Massive Bed Hounstout Marls	*Crendonites gorei* Not yet satisfactorily zoned
UPPER JURASSIC	KIMMERIDGE CLAY 800 feet	Hounstout Clay *Rhynchonella* Marls *Lingula* Shales *Rotunda* Nodules Crushed Ammonoid Shales 400 feet of clays with stone bands; Oil Shale 150 feet from base Yellow Ledge Lower Clays of Hen Cliff, 60 feet Maple Ledge Clays above and below The Flats, 120 feet	*Pavlovia rotunda* *Pectinatites pectinatus* *Subplanites* *Gravesia gigas* *Aulacostephanus pseudomutabilis*

The **Purbeck Beds** are essentially freshwater deposits formed in a delta. Calcareous matter was precipitated in shallow lagoons, sometimes crowded with Ostracods, sometimes with freshwater molluscs. Slight elevation gave rise to soils (dirt beds) in which cycads and conifers took root. The marls with gypsum point to the evaporation of sea-water, and temporary marine invasions are indicated by the oyster-bed known as the Cinder and other bands with marine shells. The Purbeck Marble, widely used by mediæval masons, is a mass of shells of the freshwater snail, *Viviparus* (*Paludina*).

The **Wealden Beds** too are of freshwater origin, but are not calcareous like most of the Purbeck. The Wealden clays, sands and grits are estimated at 2,350 feet in Swanage Bay, but they thin rapidly westward, as do the Purbeck Beds also. Some lignite occurs, representing masses of vegetation on the way to coal, and in places shells of *Viviparus, Unio, Cyrena,* and Cyprids are abundant.

In Swanage Bay, as in the Isle of Wight and the Weald, it appears that the sea returned in Aptian times with as little disturbance as when it receded. No tilting or erosion of the older beds is seen at the base of the Lower Greensand; there seems to be continuous deposition from Wealden, through Lower Greensand to Gault. But westward, as well as northward, the Albian rocks overlap the Aptian and then overstep in succession the Wealden and the whole of the Jurassics, so that the Gault rests on Trias in East Devon (p. 11). The folding and erosion of the Wealden and Jurassic beds were pre-Aptian, although, owing to the overlap, the unconformity generally appears at the base of the Albian.

At Punfield Cove, in Swanage Bay, the **Lower Greensand** has a pebbly base, followed by brown Atherfield Clay and then by sands and sandstones, 200 feet thick in all. The exposure is largely grassed over, and the sections at Worbarrow Bay and Mupe Bay are no better; they show, however, that the deposit is thinning out, and it disappears between Mupe Bay and Lulworth Cove.

The Albian also shows a pebbly base overlying the Lower Greensand in Worbarrow Bay so there may be some post-Aptian erosion. The lower part, mapped as **Gault**, is a clayey sand; the rest, **Upper Greensand,** is sand with some cherty stone towards the top. The usual *Exogyra conica* occurs, with *Pecten asper,* and glauconite grains are present in the sand, though not abundant enough to form a conspicuously green sand.

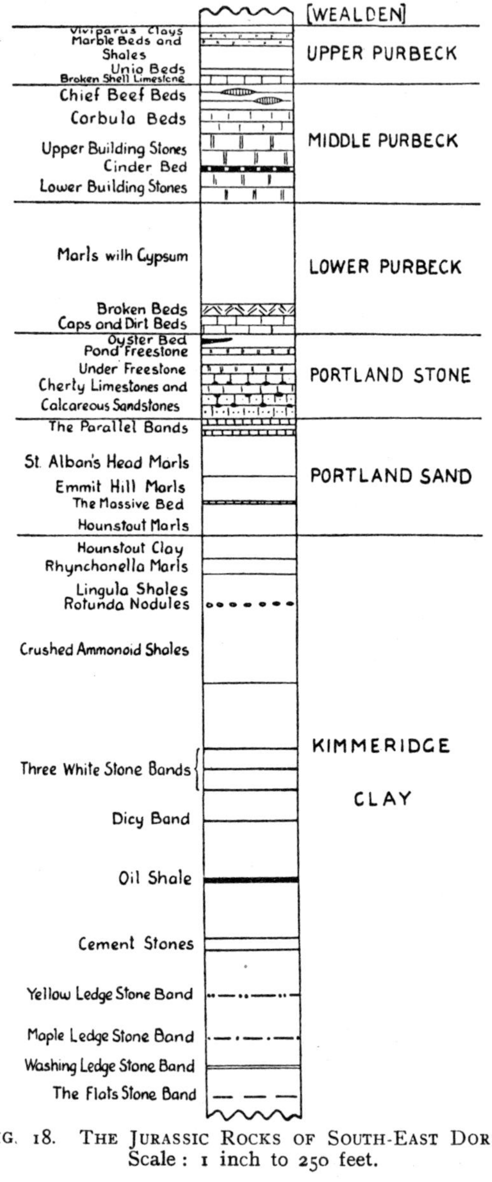

FIG. 18. THE JURASSIC ROCKS OF SOUTH-EAST DORSET
Scale : 1 inch to 250 feet.

The **Chalk** begins with the Chloritic Marl (really glau-conitic), which yields good fossiliferous sections in Swanage Bay, near Durdle Door, and at White Nothe. The grey marl with *Actinocamax plenus* is conspicuous about 35 feet above the base of the Chalk. Terrigenous matter then becomes progressively rarer, much of the Upper Chalk containing 98 or 99 per cent. $CaCO_3$. Flints occur in more or less regular bands in the Upper Chalk; some of them yield traces of the sponges from the spicules of which the silica was derived. Although the Chalk contains foraminifera, as well as larger organisms, it has little analogy with the *Globigerina* ooze of modern oceans. The bulk of it is a fine calcitic mud, appar-ently precipitated in a wide but shallow sea, into which no big rivers discharged terrigenous material.

The Eocene Beds are better developed than in Mid-Dorset. Near Studland the **Reading Beds** consist of white sand and a little mottled clay, and the **London Clay** is loamy.

The **Bagshot Beds** underlie the heath lands about Poole Harbour and include coarse and fine sands and valuable beds of ball clay and pipe clay. They become gravelly toward the west and indicate a river flowing eastward and bearing not only gravel and sand, but also clay from the kaolinised granites of Devon and Cornwall. The clay became plastic in transit; hence its properties and uses are different from those of the original kaolin.

That the Oligocene Beds of the Hampshire and Isle of Wight basin once extended into Dorset, is shown by a tiny outlier of **Bembridge Limestone** that caps the Bagshot Sand of Creechbarrow, $2\frac{1}{2}$ miles west of Corfe Castle (Hudleston, 1902; Keeping, 1910.) There is no section, but the views from Creechbarrow, 637 feet above sea-level, and from the Purbeck Hills on the way thither, repay a visit.

Blown Sand borders the shore of Studland Bay, and **Alluvium** occurs around Poole Harbour and in some of the stream valleys. **Calcareous tufa** is seen near Blashenwell Farm, a mile south of Corfe Castle; it was deposited by spring water saturated with lime from the Upper Purbecks and contains Mesolithic flints and charcoal. Peaty bogs occur in some of the hollows of Bagshot Sand, where water may be held up by iron pan forming a little below the surface of the ground.

The structure of the area is simple; the **Isle of Purbeck monocline** dominates the whole of it. The movement that caused this was post-Cretaceous, and post-Oligocene, and was connected with the Cainozoic revolution that terminated the

long Mesozoic period of quiet evolution and gave rise to the
London Basin, the Weald, the Pyrenees, the Alps and the
Himalayas. The southern limb of the monocline dips very
gently southward. Northward, the dip is gentle at first, then
becomes steeper, till the Chalk in places is vertical or even
inverted by the pressure from the south. In the Eocene tract
the dip flattens out and then reverses to a gentle southerly dip.

The monoclinal axis, like that of the Weymouth anticline,
pitches to the east. Hence the Kimmeridge Clay is seen only
in the western half of the Isle of Purbeck, while in the Isle of
Wight, on the continuation of the same monocline, the top of
the Wealden is the lowest bed left above sea-level.

FIG. 19. TWO SECTIONS THROUGH THE ISLE OF PURBECK.
I. Near Kimmeridge. II. Through Swanage.

Scale : 1 inch to 1 mile horizontally. 3 inches to 1 mile vertically.

15. Oligocene Beds.	10. Upper Greensand.	5. Middle Purbeck.
14. Bagshot Beds.	9. Gault.	4. Lower Purbeck.
13. London Clay	8. Lower Greensand.	3. Portland Stone.
12. Reading Beds.	7. Wealden Beds.	2. Portland Sand.
11. Chalk.	6. Upper Purbeck.	1. Kimmeridge Clay.

F Faults. T Isle of Purbeck thrust fault.

The intense pressure found some relief in fracture and
overthrusting. The **Isle of Purbeck fault** is seen in the
cliff near Ballard Point (*Fig.* 33), where Chalk has been thrust
southward, on a curved dislocation parallel to the bedding,
over vertical Chalk, which is crushed, slickensided, and infil-
trated with secondary calcite. Further west, the fault divides
into a number of minor fractures, as may be seen in Durdle
Cove. Here, too, soft beds in the Wealden and Purbecks are
squeezed out.

Another fault occurs at Ulwell, where a strong spring
rises in the fault-plane and the fault-shattered Chalk has been

PLATE IV.

A. DURDLE DOOR.

The arch is cut in vertical Portland Stone. Purbeck and Wealden Beds form the ridge on the left. Chalk fallen from the cliffs is seen in the foreground.

B. A STONE QUARRY, PORTLAND.

The Freestone Series of the Portland Stone capped by Lower Purbeck Beds. The overburden is stacked up in the worked-out portion of the quarry.

PLATE V.

A. "The Fossil Forest," Lulworth.

The two cylindrical masses are calcareous tufa formed round tree stumps
in the Lower Purbeck.

B. Fault in Hobarrow Bay.

The Flats stone band (a), seen rising in the cliff on the left, is let down
in two stages to form the ledge in the right foreground. Maple Ledge
Stone band (b) is seen in the cliff on the right.

eroded to a valley, utilised by the road from Swanage to Studland. Minor faults occur in Durlston Bay, and between that
and St. Alban's Head; while the shore near Kimmeridge shows
a score of faults, the effects of which on the stone bands show
up with diagrammatic clearness both in vertical section and
in plan.

The structure, and the unequal resistance to erosion of
the beds exposed, are reflected in the topography, hard rocks
in general forming hill ranges and promontories, while softer
ones are eroded to valleys and bays. The Kimmeridge Clay
forms low meadow-land overlooked on the north and east by
lofty escarpments of Portland Sand and Stone. That the sea
has not swept it all away is due to the stone bands it contains,
which offer a stubborn resistance to the waves and compel
them to break before they reach the cliffs. The Portland Stone
tends to be undercut by the rapid erosion of the Portland Sand
and to form mural scarps, as in Gad Cliff and Emmit Hill. It
forms the sheer cliffs at Lulworth and from St. Alban's Head
to Durlston Head. The Purbeck limestones form the bleak

FIG. 20. THE GAP AT CORFE CASTLE.
(From a photograph, looking north-west.)
Two streams, after draining the Wealden area in the foreground, turn northward and cut valleys through the Chalk
of the Purbeck Hills, uniting on the northern side. The
two valleys isolate the hill on which Corfe Castle stands.

upland about Worth Matravers and the dip-slope to the north,
while the unconsolidated Wealden Beds give rise to a long
valley, with ridges formed by the grit bands, which is terminated by Worbarrow Bay and Swanage Bay. The Chalk is
reduced by the high dip to a width of a quarter of a mile and
forms the Purbeck Hills, to the north of which lie the broad
heathlands of the Bagshot Sand outcrop.

Water-bearing strata include the Portland Sands, but
only small springs issue from them at Encombe and Coombe

F

Bottom, where they dip southward. The Purbeck Beds also yield some water. Swanage draws its water supply from the Chalk at Ulwell, where the fault throws out a strong spring. Near Church Knowle a spring issues from the base of the Chalk. Other springs in the Chalk may be seen on the shore at Studland, Arish Mell and Lulworth Cove.

The Kimmeridge Clay area drains southward by streams that have been rejuvenated by the recession of the coast line. In the Wealden vale, only tiny streams flow direct to the sea at Worbarrow and Swanage; the bulk of the area drains toward Corfe Castle, the two streams from west and east uniting on the north side of the Chalk outcrop and isolating the hill on which the castle stands. This drainage must have been initiated at the time when the Purbeck monocline was uplifted, a stream flowing northward on the dip-slope of Eocene Beds. Later, the Chalk emerged and stood out as the Purbeck Hills, while the softer Eocene and Wealden Beds were eroded on either side. From Lulworth to Kimmeridge the coast is under Army control.

EXCURSIONS ROUND SWANAGE.

The following are some suggestions for a week spent at Swanage. The order of the routes, and the direction in which they are taken, must depend on the state of the tide. It is essential to ascertain this before venturing along the shore at Kimmeridge.

FIRST DAY. PEVERIL POINT AND DURLSTON BAY.

This forms a good introductory half-day on arriving at Swanage. After noting the structure of the district seen from the open space at the end of Victoria Avenue (p. 107), walk to Peveril Point and along the shore of Durlston Bay, returning by the path up the cliff near the faults in the middle of the bay. Walking distance three miles (pp. 103-107).

SECOND DAY. SWANAGE, DANCING LEDGE, ANVIL POINT.

Walk south-west over the Purbeck dip-slope, past many small inclined shafts whence the building stone is, or has been, drawn up by primitive horse-whims. Continue to Dancing Ledge, and then follow the cliff path eastward to Anvil Point, Tilly Whim, and Swanage. Walking distance six miles (pp. 101-103).

THIRD DAY. ST. ALBAN'S HEAD AND WINSPIT.

By road four miles west to the Sheepsleights quarry at Coombe Bottom, where the whole of the Portland Stone, with some Lower Purbeck, is quarried. Walk down the valley to the cliffs below West Hill and Emmit Hill, where the Portland Sands are exposed. Then up to St. Alban's Head and along the cliff path to Winspit quarries in Portland Stone. Walk up the valley, noting cultivation terraces, to Worth Matravers, returning thence along the Priest's Way to Swanage. Walking distance nine miles (pp. 98-101).

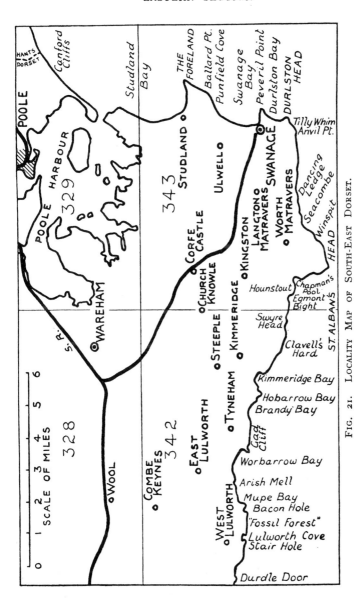

Fig. 21. LOCALITY MAP OF SOUTH-EAST DORSET.
Scale: 1 inch to 3 miles.
Showing boundaries of the one-inch maps of the Geological Survey,
Sheets 328, 329, 342, 343.

FOURTH DAY. CHAPMAN'S POOL, HOUNSTOUT, CORFE CASTLE.

By road to Worth Matravers, four miles west. Walk W. and S. to Chapman's Pool, where the upper part of the Kimmeridge Clay is exposed. Follow the shore round Egmont Point to Egmont Bight, then up to Hounstout Cliff for Portland Sands.

Walk north to Kingston and Blashenwell Farm, for calcareous tufa (p. 71), and on to Corfe Castle. Return by road or rail. Walking distance six miles (pp. 97-98).

FIFTH DAY. KIMMERIDGE BAY AND WORBARROW BAY.

By road to Kimmeridge, nine miles west. Walk down to the bay and westward along the shore to Hobarrow Bay and Brandy Bay. Thence ascend the undercliff, bearing eastward, and turn west along the top of Gad Cliff to Worbarrow Bay. Return by road from Tyneham. Walking distance five miles (pp. 91-94).

SIXTH DAY. THE LULWORTH COAST.

By road to Lulworth Cove, eighteen miles west. Walk west, by road and path, to St. Oswald's Bay, and along the shore to Durdle Door and Durdle Cove. Return by cliff path to Lulworth, walk round the Cove, and along the cliff eastward to the Fossil Forest and Mupe Bay. Then back to Lulworth Cove, and spend what time remains in Stair Hole. Return by road. Walking distance six miles (pp. 81-89).

SEVENTH DAY. BALLARD POINT AND STUDLAND.

By boat, four miles, to Studland, noting Isle of Purbeck fault in cliff near Ballard Point See Eocene section east of Studland, and the Agglestone. Return by cliff path round the Foreland and over Ballard Down. Walking distance seven miles (pp. 109-112).

EIGHTH DAY. SWANAGE BAY.

Walk north along the shore, past a long series of Wealden deposits. At Punfield Cove the Lower Greensand comes on, and the cliff beyond shows tumbled masses of fossiliferous Chloritic Marl and Chalk. Return by cliff path. Walking distance four miles (pp. 107-109).

WHITE NOTHE TO DURDLE COVE.

(2 miles. Six-inch maps, Dorset, 54 N.W., 54 N.E.)

From beyond Lyme Regis to Ringstead Bay, with the exception of the Isle of Portland, it has been possible to walk along the shore all the way, at least at some states of the tide. But from White Nothe eastward, where the cliffs are of Chalk or Portland Stone, such progress is checked by projecting points that cannot be rounded even at low water, or by long stretches of cliff running down sheer into the sea, as from St. Alban's Head to Durlston Head. Only where the soft Wealden and Eocene beds fringe the shore are there extensive beaches. Although the cliffs are described here as a continuous section, it must be borne in mind that they are accessible at certain points only. A boat is the most convenient means of access to the greater part of this section.

White Nothe is a headland of Chalk, 500 feet high. Below it are the best sections for collecting Chalk fossils on the Dorset coast, for the rock is not crushed and impregnated as it is farther east where the cliffs are close to the line of the Isle of Purbeck overthrust. The following account is based on Rowe's detailed description of the White Chalk of the Dorset Coast (1901). In the cliff sections (*Figs.* **22** and **32**) the zonal boundaries are only diagrammatic.

The Coastguard Signal Station at the top of White Nothe stands on Chalk of the *cor-anguinum* zone, with *Marsupites* Chalk exposed 100 yards to the east. From the Signal a zig-zag path descends to the top of the undercliff, traversing the *cor-anguinum, cor-testudinarium,* and *planus* zones. All these are flinty chalk, the lines of flint being more regular in the *cor-anguinum* zone than in those below. The two *Micraster* zones are somewhat ironstained, especially *cor-testudinarium.* The *Holaster planus* chalk, on the other hand, is marly and greyish in colour. Yellow bands of nodular chalk occur in it and pass up into the other two zones, but there is no true Chalk Rock, and the characteristic fauna of that horizon is also wanting.

Turning north-westward along the undercliff, we find another good face in the *Holaster planus* zone at the top of the talus below the adjoining bluff. The zone of *Terebratulina gracilis* is practically flintless. That of *Rhynchonella cuvieri* is nodular chalk with one line of flints near the top. Then, the beds dipping gently to the E.N.E., we reach the grey, marly *Actinocamax plenus* chalk, *Holaster subglobosus* chalk, also marly, and the Chloritic Marl with *H. subglobosus* abundant at its base. This is only 3 feet thick and rests on the cherty beds of the Upper Greensand.

We now pass to the shore section, which is best reached by boat. The Chert Beds form a small bench projecting into the sea below the southern point of White Nothe, and above them the Lower Chalk comes on. The beds are at first nearly ⎯⎯⎯⎯⎯⎯⎯⎯⎯ as we go eastward they begin to dip in the same ⎯⎯⎯⎯ ly at first and then more steeply, toward a ⎯⎯⎯ dle Bottom.

⎯⎯⎯ ly banded appearance of the foot of White ⎯⎯⎯ the alternation of hard and soft layers in the ⎯⎯⎯ ne. The grey *plenus* marls are clearly distin- ⎯⎯⎯ ese disappear eastward below sea-level and are

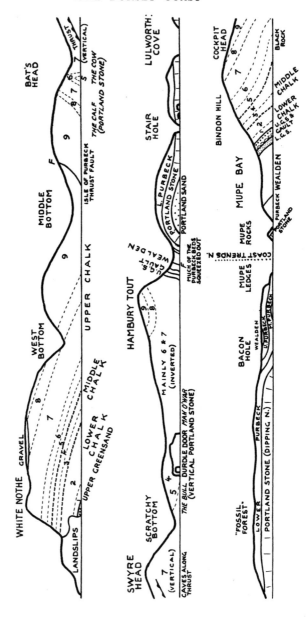

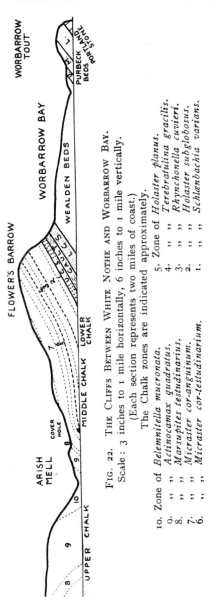

FIG. 22. THE CLIFFS BETWEEN WHITE NOTHE AND WORBARROW BAY.
Scale : 3 inches to 1 mile horizontally, 6 inches to 1 mile vertically.
(Each section represents two miles of coast.)
The Chalk zones are indicated approximately.

10. Zone of *Belemnitella mucronata.*
9. ,, ,, *Actinocamax quadratus.*
8. ,, ,, *Marsupites testudinarius.*
7. ,, ,, *Micraster cor-anguinum.*
6. ,, ,, *Micraster cor-testudinarium.*

5. Zone of *Holaster planus.*
4. ,, ,, *Terebratulina gracilis.*
3. ,, ,, *Rhynchonella cuvieri.*
2. ,, ,, *Holaster subglobosus.*
1. ,, ,, *Schlœnbachia varians.*

succeeded by hard nodular chalk of the *cuvieri* zone, 76 feet thick, containing some pyritic nodules but few fossils.

The first line of flints is taken by Rowe as the base of the *gracilis* zone, which is here 58 feet thick. It contains marly bands and also a 5-foot band of yellowish-green nodules which had been mistaken for the Chalk Rock prior to Rowe's work. The true Chalk Rock, in the *planus* zone, does not occur on the Dorset coast. The *gracilis* zone forms a big ledge sloping into the sea which cannot be climbed over except at very low tide ; at other times a boat is needed. At the back of this ledge is a small vertical bluff which Rowe found to be a good collecting ground.

The *planus* zone, 51 feet of grey and flinty chalk with nodular bands, extends eastward to the foot of the fine crag known as the Fountain Rock, 300 feet high, on the west side of **West Bottom.**

The zones of *Micraster cor-testudinarium,* 113 feet thick, and *M. cor-anguinum,* 171 feet, are both very barren. The latter shows large iron-stained patches. Between West Bottom and **Middle Bottom** the chalk of this zone begins to dip more steeply and exhibits small overthrust faults, or slide-planes, connected with the great Isle of Purbeck thrust.

The *Marsupites* zone, 111 feet thick, with irregular lines of flint, is seen between the first and third slide-planes, and then for over half a mile *quadratus* chalk forms the cliff. It is the highest zone exposed here. Flint lines are still abundant in it. Beyond the Middle Bottom syncline the beds turn up sharply and appear greatly shattered and slickensided. Somewhere between Middle Bottom and Bat's Head the east-west Isle of Purbeck overthrust fault intersects the cliff obliquely, but the exact point cannot be determined as the fault seems to have split up into a multitude of minor slide-planes.

The *Marsupites* and *Micraster* zones, now dipping steeply northward, reappear in the cliff as we near **Bat's Head,** the seaward face of which is in hard vertical chalk of the *Holaster planus* zone. The boat will be required again here, for it is not possible to walk round Bat's Head, or through Bat's Hole which penetrates it. The Calf and the Cow, two rocks lying off Bat's Head, are isolated portions of the line of vertical Portland Stone seen again at Durdle Door.

The eastward face of Bat's Head shows vertical chalk of the zones of *Holaster planus* and *Micraster cor-testudinarium.* Thence eastward for nearly half a mile the *cor-anguinum* zone is seen. At **Swyre Head,** the cliffs again reach 300 feet in height, and here two lines of thrust-faulting occur near the top of the cliff, as may be seen from a boat.

A little recess is next reached, where it is possible to climb up the cliff to **Scratchy Bottom.** On the eastern face the *cor-anguinum* chalk is seen near the head of the recess, followed on the seaward side by *cor-testudinarium,* with *planus* chalk at the tip of the little promontory. The beds here are inverted, *i.e.,* they have been tilted through more than 90° and appear to dip seaward at about 75°. A dislocation will be noticed slanting down to the south in this face of the recess; this is the slide-plane that makes a far more striking feature in the next section of cliff.

FIG. 23. CAVES ERODED ALONG A SLIDE-PLANE IN THE CHALK CLIFF WEST OF DURDLE DOOR. SWYRE HEAD AND BAT'S HEAD ARE SEEN IN THE DISTANCE.
(From a photograph.)

Beyond the little promontory lies **Durdle Cove.** Here the slide-plane just mentioned runs near the foot of the cliff and forms a plane of weakness along which the sea has hollowed out a series of little caves. The roof of each cave has been pushed northward relative to the floor, the plane of movement being re-cemented in the western part of the cove and remaining open farther east. The chalk is in the *planus* zone at first. Farther east, for a considerable distance, *planus* chalk is seen in the little projections at the foot of the cliff and again above the slide-plane, where it rests on chalk of the *cor-testudinarium* zone. Then, as the coast curves out toward the Durdle promontory, we find *gracilis* chalk thrust over the *planus* zone, and finally the slide-plane is wholly in *gracilis* chalk. The flintless character of this zone distinguishes it from the flinty chalk above, or rather to the north, since the beds are still vertical or inverted. The spurious " Chalk Rock " is seen as a band of yellowish nodules 20 feet from the top of this zone.

The beds become compressed and altered in the neighbourhood of the Durdle promontory, and the zones of *Terebratulina gracilis* and *Rhynchonella cuvieri* together measure only 70 feet in thickness. The grey marls with *Actinocamax plenus* are easily distinguished, and serve to demonstrate two slide-planes in the cliff here. They occur at shore-level near the mouth of the recess behind the wall-like projection formed by the Upper

FIG. 24. VERTICAL PLENUS MARLS (P) DIS-
PLACED BY TWO SLIDE-PLANES, ONE AT
THE BASE OF THE CLIFF, THE OTHER
HALF-WAY UP. DURDLE COVE.
(From a photograph.)

Greensand, and are at once carried northward to form a grey hollowed-out band from the shore to half-way up the cliff, where they are again shifted north.

The *subglobosus* zone extends to the aforesaid recess, and the Chloritic Marl is well exposed, adhering to a hard band with a dyke-like outcrop at the top of the Upper Greensand.

Two isolated rocks, the Blind Cow opposite Swyre Head and the Bull off Scratchy Bottom, are in the vertical Portland Stone in which Durdle Door is cut.

DURDLE DOOR TO LULWORTH COVE.

(1½ miles. Six-inch maps, Dorset, 54 N.E. and S.E., 55 S.W.)

This stretch of coast, with its extension eastward to Mupe Bay, includes the most spectacular coastal scenery in Dorset and the clearest and most striking illustrations of tectonics, or structural geology, and of marine erosion. Structurally, it shows the northern limb of the Purbeck monocline subjected to enormous pressure from the south. The beds are tilted to high angles and even inverted, the softer ones are squeezed out and the harder ones crushed, shattered and overthrust. They offer very unequal resistance to wave-action, and differential erosion gives rise to coves and bays in the softer beds, with points and promontories in the harder ones. The massive limestones of the Portland Stone form an outer barrier to the waves. When that has been penetrated by the sea, the Purbeck and Wealden Beds are rapidly eroded until the attack is again held up by the Chalk, the inner line of defence.

Durdle Door may be reached from Lulworth Cove by walking due west along a road and then along the shore of St. Oswald's Bay. This route is not available at high tide, and the alternative is to take the path that slants up the southern face of Hambury Tout and then follows the cliff top to the Durdle promontory. There is an easy descent to Durdle Cove on the west or to Man o' War Cove on the east.

The " Door," or natural arch, has been cut by the waves in vertical Portland Stone. The stone that has disappeared may have been more jointed or fractured than the rest and so gave way sooner. Westward, the Portland Stone has been swept away, except in the outlying rocks, the Bull, the Cow, etc., which mark out its strike.

At Durdle Door the Portland Stone is only 400 feet from the Chalk. At Swanage these beds are two and a half miles apart. Three factors contribute to this approach of the two beds. First, the dip here is vertical, so that the width of outcrop of the intervening beds is no greater than their thickness. But at Swanage the intervening beds are about 3,000 feet thick. The second factor then is the steady thinning from east to west which is observable at various points in the Purbeck and the Wealden Beds. Even this will not suffice to get the whole of these beds into 400 feet, and we find as the third factor that the softer beds have been squeezed out as a result of the great pressure from the south. Thus the Upper and much of the Middle Purbeck is altogether missing in the Durdle isthmus, and no doubt the softer Wealden Beds have lost a great part of their thickness through the same process, which even affects the Chalk in the cliff behind.

Against the Portland Stone come the thin-bedded limestones of the Purbeck Beds, up to the Cinder Bed. Then follow some 200 feet of sands and clays, with a band of small pebbles of white quartz near the top. These constitute the most westerly coastal exposure of the Wealden Beds. Next come sandy clays, sands, and chert beds, with *Exogyra conica,* etc., representing the Gault and Upper Greensand, and terminating in a hard sandstone which forms a prominent feature on the west side of the isthmus. North of it the Chloritic Marl and Lower Chalk will be seen.

FIG. 25. MAN O' WAR COVE.
(From a photograph, looking west.)
Vertical Portland Stone forms the Man o' War Rock and the south side of the Durdle promontory beyond. Purbeck and Wealden Beds form most of the promontory. The cliffs are in Chalk, crushed and inverted in the foreground. Swyre Head, Bat's Head and White Nothe are seen in the distance.

The Man o' War is a large rock, composed of Portland Stone with a little Lower Purbeck, which, with several smaller ones, marks out the line of the Portland Stone from Durdle Door eastward and south-eastward to Dungy Head. **Man o' War Cove**, lying immediately east of the Durdle promontory, is less exposed to wave-action than the westward-facing Durdle Cove; consequently a talus has accumulated here, masking much of the Upper Greensand and Lower Chalk. Their up-turned edges, however, are visible at low water. Middle Chalk follows, and is seen again in Man o' War Head, while the back of this cove is in grey flinty chalk of the *Holaster planus* zone.

At **Man o' War Head** the Chalk is only 200 feet from the Portland Stone, and in this part of the cliff the crushing is intense. The beds are inverted and appear to dip south-ward, the real dip being expressed as 110° or 120° to the north. The *Holaster planus* zone is squeezed into a thickness of 4 or 5 feet of shattered chalk; while some of the flints have been crushed to powder and drawn out into black streaks " like so much coal dust," as Strahan remarks.

The *Micraster* zones are the highest seen in **St. Oswald's Bay**, with the usual red patches in the *cor-anguinum* chalk. The western side of the bay is a repetition of Durdle Cove, and we pass in succession vertical chalk of the *planus, gracilis* and *cuvieri* zones. Even the thrusting seen in Durdle Cove is repeated on a small scale. Then follow the Lower Chalk, Upper Greensand and Gault, resting on an eroded surface of Wealden clays and sands, with some lignite and white quartz pebbles. These are inverted and reduced in thickness by the squeez-ing out of some of the beds. Near **Dungy Head** the Wealden is faulted against the Middle Purbeck. Part of the Lower Purbeck is also faulted out. The Portland Stone at Dungy Head is no longer vertical but dips northward at about 45°.

From Dungy Head eastward for a mile and a half the cliffs are of Portland Stone and are washed by the tide even at low water. The shore is only accessible at a few places. It is therefore necessary to leave St. Oswald's Bay by climbing up over the Wealden Beds and following the path toward Lul-worth Cove, turning to the right just before reaching it to visit Stair Hole.

In **Stair Hole** the fine section in contorted Purbeck Beds first strikes the visitor's eye. The massive Portland Stone dips steadily northward, followed by the thin-bedded Lower Purbeck. The upper beds of this show a minor anticline near shore-level, while the Middle Purbeck shows two anticlines, the northern limbs being vertical or overfolded.

The sea, having penetrated the barrier of Portland Stone in three places, is attacking the fractured Purbeck Beds. When they are gone, the soft Wealden Beds will soon be swept away, and it will not be long, geologically speaking, before Stair Hole joins Lulworth Cove.

LULWORTH COVE TO MUPE BAY.

(1½ miles.   Six-inch map, Dorset, 55 S.W.)

Lulworth Cove is a beautiful example of marine erosion in rocks of very unequal resistance.   The entrance to the cove is a breach, 400 feet wide, in the Portland Stone, which, as we have already seen, is the chief bulwark against the waves on this stretch of coast.   The overlying Purbeck Beds have been cut back at an angle, until sheltered by the Portland Stone, and the incoherent sands and clays of the Wealden have been swept out by the sea to a width of 1,400 feet.   Northward, the attack is held up by a steep face of Chalk, over 300 feet high.   The cove is not quite 1,000 feet from north to south, but seen from the side it appears more nearly circular than it is in reality.   It will be noticed that the Wealden Beds offer as little resistance to sub-aerial as to marine erosion, and their outcrop forms a valley between the Chalk on the north and the Purbeck-Portland ridge on the south (*Plate* I).

A good general view of Lulworth Cove is obtained from the high ground (119 feet) above the West Point, and a corresponding position beyond Stair Hole gives a view of the two coves.

The road and stream reach the shore at Lulworth Cove close to the outcrop of the Gault and Upper Greensand. These dip north at about 45°.   The outcrop crosses the cove beneath the shingle, and at the Black Rocks copious springs appear at the junction of the Upper Greensand and Chalk, near high-water mark.

The **Chalk** face is badly masked by slipped material and talus, wave erosion in this sheltered cove being slow compared with the work of the sub-aerial agents.   Some collecting can be done from fallen blocks of Chalk.   The *plenus* Marl can be traced across the face, and the Chloritic Marl is also in evidence.

The **Upper Greensand** has a little sand with brown chert at the top, then more sand, becoming darker and more clayey below (" Gault "), the whole being about 130 feet thick. The Lower Greensand is missing, and the Gault, with a pebbly base, rests on an eroded surface of Wealden Beds.

The **Wealden** is best seen on the east side of Lulworth Cove, the upper part being cut out by a strike fault on the western side.   The thickness appears to be about 570 feet, but some of the beds show signs of squeezing.   A coarse grit with lignite and pebbles of white quartz up to half an inch in length

occurs rather above the middle; it can be traced from the
Durdle promontory to Mupe Bay. Near the base is a black

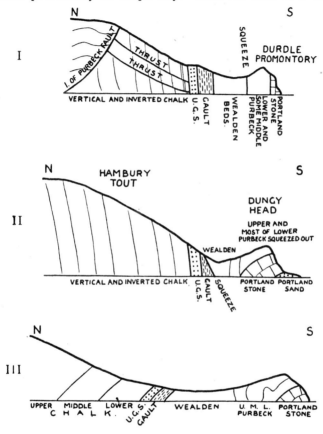

FIG 26. SECTIONS FROM NORTH TO SOUTH. I. THROUGH THE
DURDLE PROMONTORY. II. THROUGH DUNGY HEAD.
III. WEST OF LULWORTH COVE.
Scale : 12 inches to 1 mile.

carbonaceous sand, and oil-sands also occur. The lower beds of
the Wealden are over-folded, with a dip of 110°.

The **Upper Purbeck** also is inverted, though the disturbance is not so marked as in Stair Hole. Most of the clays
that separate the limestones at Bacon Hole appear to have

been squeezed out. The Cinder Bed, a mass of small oyster shells in the **Middle Purbeck**, is the lowest bed affected by the disturbance. This and two other limestones form ledges on the shore, dry at low water. In the **Lower Purbeck**, the Broken Beds will be noticed, and the Soft and Hard Caps, the latter resting on the **Portland Stone.**

Leaving Lulworth Cove by a path over the Wealden Beds and walking south-east to the edge of the cliff, we come to a wide ledge below the cliff top some 500 yards east of the Cove. It is easily reached by scrambling down the sloped outcrop of Lower Purbeck Beds; the Portland Stone below drops sheer into deep water.

The floor of the ledge is formed of the Hard and Soft Caps. The former is unusually thick here, and its junction with the Portland Stone may be seen by looking over the edge. At its base is an impersistant dirt bed, and another, the Main Dirt Bed, separates the two Caps. These dirt beds represent old land-surfaces, with dark soil and limestone pebbles. Both Caps are formed of a hard tufaceous limestone, and the upper surface of the Soft Cap shows large bosses (" burrs ") of tufa deposited around the stumps and fallen trunks of trees that grew in the underlying dirt bed. The trees themselves are silicified and may be seen within the burrs where they have not been removed by collectors or other agents of destruction. They form the " **Fossil Forest** " of local repute (*Plate* V. A).

Above the Soft Caps come the Broken Beds, 10 or 12 feet of shattered limestones. Their smashed condition is no local incident; it is a constant feature from Durdle Door to Durlston Bay, though rarely so well seen as here. Osmond Fisher in 1856 attributed it to the beds having collapsed into hollows produced by the decay of the vegetation of the old forest that they had overwhelmed, and therefore dating from Purbeck times; but H. B. Woodward regarded the Broken Beds as a crush-breccia due to sliding of the overlying beds when the Purbeck monocline was formed. The shattering may be due to expansion of anhydrite on passing into gypsum, and solution of the gypsum. The Broken Beds pass up into undisturbed Cypris Freestone, but the rest of the section is not clear.

Half a mile east of the Fossil Forest comes a great gap in the protective line of the Portland Stone. The ruined barrier may be seen in the Mupe Rocks, some of which have some Lower Purbeck adhering; then for a mile and a half it is entirely destroyed, though known to the fishermen as a line of submerged reefs, reappearing in Worbarrow Tout and Gad Cliff. We have seen the beginning of the attack with the

PLATE VI.

B   A PURBECK STONE QUARRY.
Showing inclined shaft, block of stone on carriage, and
horse whim.

A.   CLIFF EAST OF LULWORTH COVE.
B, Broken Beds of the Lower Purbeck; S, Soft Cap;
D, Dirt Bed; H, Hard Cap; P, Portland Stone.

PLATE VII.

A. CLIFF BETWEEN BALLARD POINT AND THE FORELAND.
Showing one of the Pinnacles, and Old Harry in the distance.

B. CHERT BED IN THE MIDDLE PURBECK, DURLSTON BAY.
Thin veins of calcite traverse both limestone and chert alike.

breaching of the barrier in Stair Hole; Lulworth Cove shows the limit of effective wave action with a single narrow gap in the barrier; the union of adjacent coves is seen in Man o' War Cove and St. Oswald's Bay; and here in **Worbarrow Bay** we have the culmination of an attack on a wide front, only held up by the second line of defence, the Chalk. We shall see later that the Chalk itself has been swept away by the sea between the Foreland and the Needles in the Isle of Wight; but in that case the sea had outflanked the first line of defence, for the easterly pitch of the Isle of Purbeck monocline would bring the Portland Stone below sea-level beyond Durlston Head; while the Chalk itself may have been breached by a stream valley, like the gap at Corfe Castle, before the sea reached it.

Bacon Hole, the little cove first reached, shows a complete section of the Purbeck Beds. At the seaward side, and in Mupe Rocks, the Portland Stone is seen, dipping north at about $25°$. At its junction with the Purbeck Beds a cave has been formed by the removal of slabs of the Hard Cap. Brecciation is not confined to the Broken Beds; in places the Soft Cap below and the Cypris Freestone above are much fractured. There are conspicuous hard bands in the Middle Purbeck, some of which run out as ledges on the shore. The Cinder Bed, Upper Freestone and Broken Shell Limestone formed a natural breakwater on the south side of Mupe Bay, but have been quarried down to sea-level. We may regard this feature as the analogue of Peveril Point at Swanage.

The uppermost Purbeck, seen in the slopes of Bacon Hole and in the south part of **Mupe Bay,** is mainly clays, often with abundant *Viviparus,* and some thin bands of *Viviparus* limestone or " marble." The Upper Purbeck is 50 feet thick here, the Middle Purbeck is 57 feet, and the Lower 143 feet; 250 feet in all.

The base of the Wealden, as seen at the top of the slope in Bacon Hole, consists of laminated clays and sands.

MUPE BAY TO WORBARROW BAY.

(3 miles. Six-inch maps, Dorset 55 N.W. and S.W.)

These two bays, with Arish Mell, constitute a wide bight, with Chalk at the back, Wealden Beds forming most of the sides, and Purbeck Beds and Portland Stone at the points.

Starting at **Mupe Ledge,** formed, as we have seen, of limestones of Middle and Upper Purbeck age, we find in Mupe Bay soft **Upper Purbecks** followed by equally incoherent

Wealden Beds. Lignite is common in the lower half of the Wealden, and the line of white quartz pebbles is again found in the upper half. These beds occupy the greater part of the coastline in Mupe Bay.

Just before the **Chalk** cliff is reached, narrow outcrops of Lower Greensand, Gault and Upper Greensand are intersected by the coast, but the section is obscured by a scree from the Chalk cliff above. The Lower Greensand makes its first appearance here, being overlapped by the Gault farther to the west. It does not differ markedly from some of the Wealden sands, and is unfossiliferous.

The junction of the Upper Greensand and the base of the Chalk is not clear. The shore is accessible as far as **Black Rock,** the Chalk ranging up to the zone of *Micraster cortestudinarium,* which forms most of that promontory and the cave to the west of it.

Here, unless a boat is available, we must retrace our steps to the Wealden slopes, ascend 460 feet by the path over Bindon Hill, and reach the shore again at Arish Mell.

The shore between Black Rock and **Arish Mell** should only be visited on a falling tide, for the sea runs up very quickly below Cockpits Head. The Chalk, still dipping steeply north, shows the two *Micraster* zones followed by that of *Marsupites*. Chalk of the zone of *Actinocamax quadratus* stretches from nearly opposite Barber's Rock to a low bluff in the west side of Arish Mell. Rowe gives its thickness as 354 feet; he found it particularly fossiliferous in the western part, but not in Arish Mell.

The low cliff west of the little stream that enters the bay is in the zone of *Belemnitella mucronata,* with the zonal fossil fairly common. A strong spring will be found close to the mouth of the stream.

Eastward, *quadratus* Chalk is first met with in the cliff, then the comparatively narrow band of the *Marsupites* zone, while the *Micraster* zones form most of the eastern side of Arish Mell, the lines of flint showing up the dip admirably. The bedding is somewhat disturbed, and slickensided surfaces are common. The Isle of Purbeck thrust-plane cannot be far inland. Cover Hole, the seaward cave, is in inaccessible *planus* Chalk. Arish Mell therefore shows Chalk of six zones, from *Holaster planus* up to *Belemnitella mucronata.*

From Cover Hole to Cow Corner the shore is inaccessible. The cliff runs nearly along the strike and is at first in the zone of *Holaster planus,* then in **Terebratulina gracilis** and *Rhyn-*

chonella cuvieri. These last two form ledges running along-shore.

At **Cow Corner** the Lower Chalk with the Chloritic Marl is seen. Flints occur near the base, an unusual feature in the Lower Chalk. Eastward, the **Upper Greensand** appears, green and sandy for the most part, with lumps full of *Exogyra conica* and other fossils. There are no chert beds. The lower part is as usual more clayey, with a basal conglomerate, and is called Gault, though here again there is no evidence of anything higher than the Lower Gault in either the Gault or the Upper Greensand.

Next, with a marked line of erosion at the top, comes the **Lower Greensand,** some 130 feet of sands and clays with ironstone. Springs of chalybeate water occur on the beach, near the middle of the Lower Greensand.

Wealden Beds form the cliffs for the next half-mile—sands, marls and clays, with lignite and coarse quartz-grit, the whole about 1,200 feet thick. The site of the Coastguard cottages at Worbarrow is on the Upper Purbeck clays and bands of limestone with *Viviparus.* The *Unio* Beds form a steep face 12 yards south of the Lifeboat House. **Worbarrow Tout** is mainly in Middle Purbeck, with the Cinder Bed well exposed, and its seaward side is in Lower Purbeck and Portland Stone.

GAD CLIFF TO KIMMERIDGE BAY.

(3 miles. Six-inch map, Dorset, 55 S.E.)

The Portland Stone, lost beneath the waters of Worbarrow Bay, reappears in the southern side of **Worbarrow Tout,** but it is penetrated again almost immediately in the cove called **Pondfield,** where the sea has cut back to the Lower and Middle Purbeck. Here, about ten feet above the base of the Purbeck, is a tufaceous limestone having cavities lined with quartz and yielding perfect quartz crystals when dissolved in acid.

The Portland Stone reappears in the eastern cheek of Pondfield and, with a capping of Lower Purbeck, ascends from sea-level to form the magnificent crags of **Gad Cliff,** reaching an elevation of 550 feet in Tyneham Cap. It is not quarried, for the valuable freestones found farther east have either died out or become cherty. Beneath the crags appear the Portland Sand and the Kimmeridge Clay, the coast running eastward, nearly along the strike, for a mile. This is an unattractive

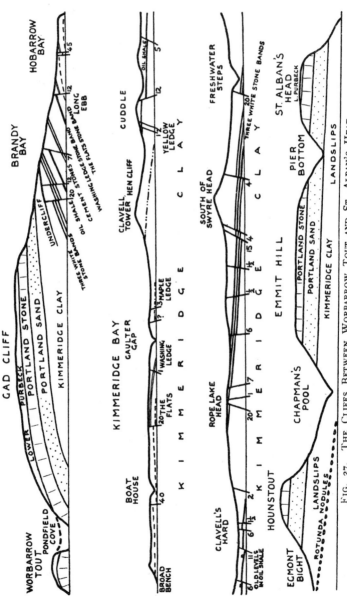

FIG. 27. THE CLIFFS BETWEEN WORBARROW TOUT AND ST. ALBAN'S HEAD.
Scale: 3 inches to 1 mile horizontally, 6 inches to 1 mile vertically.
The throw of each fault, in feet, is indicated by the figure on the downthrow side.

bit of coast; the cliffs are wave-washed near Pondfield, and access from the other end is blocked by great masses of cherty limestone fallen from above, while the slopes are a trackless wilderness abounding in adders. There is a path, however, along the top of Gad Cliff, with magnificent views, and the shore may be reached from a point south of Tyneham Cap, keeping west for some distance along the undercliff, and descending where the grassy slope comes down almost to shore-level in Brandy Bay. Poor sections in the Portland Sand and the uppermost Kimmeridge Clay are seen here, but these beds are better exposed farther east, at Hounstout and Emmit Hill.

The shore of **Brandy Bay,** and thence round to Kimmeridge Bay, can be visited at low tide, bearing in mind that the cliffs can only be ascended at one intermediate point, namely, by the boathouse in the cove beyond Broad Bench. On the shore of Brandy Bay one notices rolled slabs of dark brown shale with a bituminous odour. Thin splinters will ignite in a match flame and burn with an unpleasant smell. This oil shale is the Kimmeridge " Coal " or " Blackstone." It crops out in the cliff on the north side of Brandy Bay, but is thinner here than it is east of Kimmeridge Bay. Some distance above it is a band of dense black hardened shale with a dicy fracture, Arkell's Basalt Stone Band. Higher still come three bands of hardened white shale. Fallen blocks of all these bands strew the shore. The intervening shales yield perisphinctid ammonites (*Subplanites*).

Three faults in Brandy Bay have throws of 20 feet and 12 feet to the east and 7 feet to the north-west, the dip being about 20° to the N. or N.W.

Below the Oil Shale come about 100 feet of shale, with two conspicuous bands of cementstone, still in the *Subplanites* zone. Yellow Ledge and Maple Ledge Stone Bands do not appear in this limb of the anticline. Shales with *Gravesia* follow. The first prominent reef or ledge running out across the foreshore is formed by the Washing Ledge Stone Band. This is seen rising in the cliff beyond, a double band of stone with a thin parting of shale. **Long Ebb,** separating Brandy Bay from Hobarrow Bay, is formed by a lower stone band, that of Broad Bench and the Flats.

In **Hobarrow Bay** two faults are shown with diagrammatic clearness, both in plan and section. Near the north-west corner of the bay the stone bands are seen to be thrown down about 12 feet to the east, and the adjacent shales are seamed with thin veins of calcite deposited by water traversing the fracture. The fault in the north-east corner (*Plate* V. B) throws the Flats Stone Band down in two steps, from about 40 feet up in the cliff to sea-level on the east, where it forms a ledge between tide marks, the edge of which marks roughly the course of the fault. The Washing Ledge Stone Band is brought down almost to a level with the lower band, from which it is readily distinguished by its parting.

Hobarrow Bay lies on the axis of the Isle of Purbeck anticline, a slight southerly dip appearing in Broad Bench. The fault of 45 feet brings lower beds to the surface in Hobarrow Bay than on the eastern side of the Broad Bench promontory, and we see here the lowest beds exposed in the Isle of Purbeck, belonging to the *Aulacostephanus* zone. The lowest part of the Kimmeridge Clay is not seen in this, the type locality, nor is it exposed nearer than Ringstead Bay (p. 66), nine miles westward.

The Flats Stone Band forms the wide platform known as **Broad Bench,** beyond which it slowly rises in the cliff, the dip being about 2° to the south. In the next cove, just west of the **boathouse,** it is dropped 40 feet back to sea-level by a fault which is seen in plan on the foreshore as well as in section in the cliff, the shales on the upthrow side having been eroded more than the stone band on the downthrow or eastern side. The stone band then forms a ledge at the foot of the cliff, dipping gently seaward and strewn with fallen blocks. It rises in the cliff when the shore trends north-eastward, only to be dropped again by a 20-foot fault to form **the Flats.** Here it is horizontal, but a dip to the S.E. soon sets in and carries it finally below sea-level.

Meanwhile the Washing Ledge Stone Band appears at the top of the cliff and descends, aided by a reversed fault of 1 foot, to form the long scar of **Washing Ledge** in the middle of Kimmeridge Bay. Just beyond this is the way up at Gaulter Gap.

KIMMERIDGE BAY TO CHAPMAN'S POOL.

(4 miles. Six-inch maps, Dorset, 55 S.E. and 56 S.W.)

Both Kimmeridge Bay and Chapman's Pool are easily visited at low tide, but the walk from one to the other below the cliffs is risky and should only be undertaken on a falling tide. For three miles there is no way up the cliffs, nor even a ledge on which to take refuge if cut off by the tide. The cliffs are in Kimmeridge Clay, but they are nearly vertical and quite unlike clay cliffs in general. They are formed of shales alternating with stone bands, which form ledges on the foreshore. There is a talus or beach of shale pellets, churned by the waves at high water. Hence the muddy character of the sea. The shales are bituminous and give a peculiar odour to Kimmeridge Bay, especially on a hot day.

Starting at **Gaulter Gap,** at the mouth of the streamlet that runs down from Kimmeridge, we see Washing Ledge running out at right angles to the shore. It is formed by a stone band that may be seen rising in the cliffs to the north-west, where a lower stone band forms the Flats.

A fault of unknown throw is the only feature of interest between Gaulter Gap and the eastern corner of Kimmeridge Bay. It is therefore better to begin the traverse at the latter point, where a slope leads down to Maple Ledge, a stone band dipping gently eastward. On the shore north-west of the **Clavell Tower** are the ruins of a pier which was connected by a tramway with a level and a shaft driven in or to the Kimmeridge Coal, or Blackstone. The " coal " is a band of oil shale, about 2 feet 10 inches thick including partings, which has a conchoidal fracture when fresh and burns readily with a most unpleasant smell. On weathering, the shaly laminæ separate and tend to curl up. This material appears to have been used in Roman times and earlier for making vases and such things; waste discs that have been turned on a lathe constitute the mis-called Kimmeridge coal money (see Mansel-Pleydell, 1892, 1894). Early in the eighteenth century Sir William Clavell, of Smedmore House, began to manufacture alum here, and afterwards glass and salt, using the " coal " as fuel. Later, it was tried for improving the illuminating power of coal-gas and as a source of oil, of which it is said to have yielded 66 gallons per ton on a commercial scale. During the 1914-18 War it was examined as a possible source of oil (Strahan and Pringle, 1918), but the thinness of the seam and its high sulphur content, producing a foul smell on burning, have prevented further exploitation. The fauna of the oil shale and associated shales includes *Lingula ovalis, Orbiculoidea latissima, Lucina minuscula,* and the free-swimming crinoid *Saccocoma.* The small pyritised plates of the last-named were found also in the boring at Corton, near Portisham.

In **Hen Cliff,** beyond the Clavell Tower, shales of the *Gravesia* zone are seen. The highest of the four stone bands that are prominent in this part of the Kimmeridge Clay is seen about half-way up the cliff, descending to sea-level, where it forms **Yellow Ledge.** Here there are two little faults with displacements of one and two feet.

The Kimmeridge Coal appears in the cliff top near Yellow Ledge, being about 150 feet above the Yellow Ledge Stone Band. Some 60 feet below the " coal " is a band of calcareous marl, 2½ feet thick, that was formerly worked for making cement. A second cement stone band occurs 30 feet lower.

The " coal," which also is marked by old workings in the cliff, descends to the shore beyond the headland of **Clavell's Hard** (which is not to be confused with that on which the Clavell Tower stands). The faults in this part of the cliff have throws, first of 12 feet to the east, then 5, 6, 11, and 6 feet to the west. Close to the last, below Clavell's Hard, is one of 1½ feet to the east, and 200 yards farther one of 2 feet to the west.

Below **Rope Lake Head** is an extensive group of ledges, of which the westernmost is due to what Arkell calls the Rope Lake Head Stone Band. Here, too, is a group of three faults which are not, like most of the others, strike-faults. They cross the ledges almost at right-angles, and their throws are 20 feet to the north-west, 1 foot and 7 feet to the south-east.

In the cliff of **Rope Lake Hole** a band of hard black shale, with a cuboidal fracture, descends to sea-level and runs out as the ledge bounding the Hole on the east. It is dropped 6 feet and ½ foot to the east by faults. This Arkell calls the Basalt Stone Band, with a fine disregard for petrology. The Dicy Band would be a better term, following Blake's description of such shales.

Above this band come 35 feet more of shales yielding crushed *Subplanites* (the dominant perisphinctid ammonite from below the Yellow Ledge Stone Band), and then a series of three prominent white stone bands. The lowest of these is conspicuous in the cliff between Rope Lake Head and the spur south of **Swyre Head,** where it is known to the fishermen as the Lias Rocks. It consists of hard white calcareous shale.

On the west side of the Swyre Head spur are two faults close together, with throws of 14 and 4 feet, and on the east one with a throw of 4 feet, all to the west. One hundred yards west of **Freshwater Steps** is another, the last fault in this section of coast. It has a throw of 20 feet to the west.

The shales below and above the highest of the three stone bands mentioned above yield *Pectinatites,* small crushed perisphinctids not unlike the *Subplanites* of lower levels. A band of hardened shale forms the sill of the waterfall at Freshwater

FIG. 28. HOUNSTOUT AND CHAPMAN'S POOL.
(From photographs, looking north-west.)
Crushed Ammonoid Shales of the Upper Kimmeridgian form the slabs in the foreground, and are seen rising in the cliff beyond. The *rotunda* nodules occur above. Hounstout Cliff, above the undercliff, shows the whole of the Portland Sand capped by Portland Stone.

Steps. There is no public way up the cliff here, and the bluff beyond can only be passed at quite low tide. From this point eastward there are no more stone bands, and therefore no more ledges running seaward.

Shales of the *Pectinatites* zone form most of the cliffs of **Egmont Bight** and **Egmont Point.** Here it is possible to climb up to the footpath that winds below Hounstout Cliff and joins an old road, part of which has slipped seaward.

In **Chapman's Pool** the overlying Crushed Ammonoid Shales appear, w i t h flattened white ammonites, mostly *Pavlovia rotunda.* A hard shale band forms a slippery pavement, covered with *Pavlovia,* between the stream and the b o a t h o u s e in Chapman's Pool, and, in the cliff above, the same ammonite may be seen in abundance, uncrushed, and sometimes enclosed in small nodules.

The remainder of the Kimmeridge Clay, some 90 feet, yields few ammonites and ill-preserved, and it has not yet been zoned. It is well exposed in **Hounstout Cliff,** and Arkell has given the following lithic divisions :—(1) *Lingula* Shales, dark shales with *Lingula ovalis*. (2) *Rhynchonella* Marls, grey marls with abundant *Rhynchonella* cf. *subvariabilis*. (3) Hounstout Clay, dark and unfossiliferous. This clay throws out water from the more permeable beds above, and a line of seapage at its upper surface, well seen in Hounstout Cliff, has been adopted as the top of the Kimmeridge Clay, but Arkell, following Fitton, includes the overlying Hounstout Marls and makes the Massive Bed the base of the **Portland Sand.**

The Massive Bed is a prominent six-foot band of calcareous sandstone, about 50 feet above the old road leading round the face of Hounstout. Ammonites occurring in it and the overlying Emmit Hill Marls, have been compared to a Russian form, " *Virgatites* " *scythicus*.

The White Cementstone Band, 2 feet thick, separates the Emmit Hill Marls from the St. Alban's Head Marls. Above the latter come the two very conspicuous Parallel Bands, each about 6 feet thick, separated by 10 feet of calcareous shales with thinner stone bands. Here we reach the top of the Portland Sand.

There is no satisfactory line of division between the Portland Sand and **Portland Stone,** and above the Parallel Bands are 24 feet of sandstone which are included in the Cherty Series of the Portland Stone. The sandstone is cherty in the upper part, and becomes more and more calcareous, passing through calcareous sandstone and sandy limestone to the normal limestone with chert nodules. The Freestone Series of the Portland Stone occupies the top of Hounstout, which is just over 500 feet above sea-level.

SHEEPSLEIGHTS QUARRY, ST. ALBAN'S HEAD AND WINSPIT.

(4 miles. Six-inch maps, Dorset, 56 S.W., 59 N.W., 59 N.E.)

As the Portlandian is the chief Stage exposed around St. Alban's Head, it will be well to visit first the **Sheepsleights quarry** of the Worth Stone Co. in Coombe Bottom, 1½ miles inland, reached from the Swanage road one mile east of Kingston. Here not only the Freestone Series but the Cherty

Series also is quarried for road-metal. The other quarries in the district worked the Freestone Series only.

The Sheepsleights quarry is worked in four stages, and the following details are taken from Arkell's " Jurassic System." The top stage exposes the Lower Purbeck Caps, the Shrimp Bed, and the *Titanites* Bed (Blue Stone or Spangle). The Shrimp Bed, 8 or 10 feet thick, is a fine-grained white limestone yielding a small Crustacean, probably *Callianassa*. It passes down gradually into the Blue Stone, a grey shelly limestone, 10 feet thick, full of *Trigonia gibbosa, Isognomon (Perna) bouchardi, Chlamys lamellosus, Protocardia dissimilis,* etc. Large ammonites of the genus *Titanites* are common.

The second stage from the top of the quarry shows the Pond Freestone above, resting on the Chert Vein, with the House Cap below. The Pond Freestone is a good oolitic freestone, 7 feet thick. The Chert Vein, or Flint Vein, 2 to 4 feet thick, is easily identified and marks a recurrence of the conditions in which the Cherty Series was laid down. The House Cap, 8 feet, is a coarse limestone like the Blue Stone, and like it is sometimes called Spangle, apparently from the calcite cleavages.

The third cut shows the Under Picking Cap, 2 or 3 feet of hard freestone, and the Under Freestone, 8 to 11 feet, another good oolite, much quarried in the old workings on the cliffs.

This is the bottom of the Freestone Series, or zone of *Titanites giganteus,* which is here some 50 feet thick. The lowest part of the Sheepsleights quarry is in the Cherty Series, or zone of *Kerberites pseudogigas.* The presence of chert nodules renders this series worthless as a building stone, and it forms the floor of the other quarries in the district.

We now descend Coombe Bottom and Hill Bottom toward Chapman's Pool, pass the Coastguard Station below West Hill, and reach the long stretch of undercliff on the west side of **Emmit Hill** and **St. Alban's Head.** Here the slope of Kimmeridge Clay is concealed by fallen masses of Portland Stone and Sand from the cliff above. The upper beds of the Kimmeridge Clay may be seen below Pier Bottom, the valley between Emmit Hill and St. Alban's Head. Here, too, and below West Hill, the Massive Bed is exposed in the lower part of the Portland Sand. It is a 6-foot band of hard calcareous sandstone. The Emmit Hill Marls, 30 or 40 feet thick, usually appear immediately above the talus, and above them is the White Cementstone Band, 2 feet thick. The St. Alban's Head

Marls form the next 40 feet, and the top of the Portland Sand is reached in the Parallel Bands.

The Cherty Series of the Portland Stone passes from calcareous sandstone below through sandy limestones to the normal hard limestone with chert which forms the crags of Emmit Hill and is followed by the Freestone Series.

On **St. Alban's Head,** reached by a path from Pier Bottom, the Coastguard Station and the tiny chapel stand on the Lower Purbeck.

From St. Alban's Head eastward for five miles, cliffs of Portland Stone drop sheer into the sea, and we must continue our survey from the cliff path. Sections are more numerous than might be expected, owing to the many old quarries on or near the cliff top.

Half a mile east of St. Alban's Head the Portland Sand is brought down to sea-level, and three faults close together have throws of 20 feet to the north-west and 20 feet and 15 feet to the east. The bedding is horizontal for some distance, and the Portland Sand forms a shelf at low-water mark covered with fallen blocks of Portland Stone. Another fault, with a throw of 15 feet to the east, occurs near a small old quarry below the West Man.

One mile east of St. Alban's Chapel are the extensive quarries at **Winspit.** The succession here is very similar to that at Sheepsleights quarry. The details are as follows :—

WINSPIT QUARRY.

PURBECK BEDS. Irregular limestones and clays.

PORTLAND STONE.		ft.	in.
SHRIMP BED. Fine-grained white limestone, burnt for lime		8	0
BLUE STONE (*Titanites* BED). Hard grey limestone with shells, used for gate-posts, etc.		9	0
UPPER OR POND FREESTONE. Good oolitic limestone		7	0
FLINT VEIN. Limestone with white chert		4	0
LISTY BED. Soft limestone	2 ft. to	4	0
HOUSE CAP. Coarse limestone used for breakwaters, etc.	5 ft. to	6	0
UNDER PICKING CAP. Hard stone that had to be blasted out	2 ft. to	3	0
UNDER FREESTONE. Good stone, used for sinks, kerbstones, etc. Worked in underground galleries		6	0
CLIFF BEDS. The Cherty Series.			

Both sides of the coombe that runs up from Winspit to Worth Matravers show fine series of cultivation terraces. These appear to have been made on purpose; they are too high and narrow to be due to the mere downwash of ploughed soil; yet they run round northern and southern slopes without discrimination, and the soil, on the Lower Purbeck, does not seem to be particularly fertile or likely to repay such industry.

WINSPIT TO DURLSTON HEAD.

(4 miles. Six-inch maps, Dorset, 59 N.E., 56 S.E., 57 S.W.)

Throughout this section the cliffs of Portland Stone drop sheer into the sea. There is a gentle easterly dip, counteracted by a number of faults throwing the beds down to the west. The Lower Purbeck, at or near the cliff top, has a wide outcrop in the west, narrowing eastward, and the Middle Purbeck forms high ground to the north. The Winspit and Seacombe quarries may be reached from Worth Matravers, Dancing Ledge from Swanage by crossing the dip-slope of the Middle Purbeck with its many small quarries in the Stone Beds (*Plate* VI. B).

In the cliff immediately west of Seacombe, a couple of faults drop the beds between them 10 feet, trough-wise, bringing down the Lower Purbeck to the cliff-top.

The **Seacombe quarries** show much the same beds as at Winspit (above), but the Under Freestone here attains its maximum thickness of 9 feet. On the eastern side is a fault with a throw of 4 feet to the east, and farther on are faults with throws of 20 feet and 15 feet to the west.

Passing one or two small old quarries, we reach the larger workings at **Dancing Ledge.** Here again, as at Winspit and Seacombe, the Under Freestone has been won by underground workings, the Underpicking Cap forming the roof and the Cherty Series the floor. We can examine the last at close quarters, descending to the wave-washed ledge with its giant ammonites and noting the tendency for caves to develop along the joint planes. The dip is about 4° to the south-east.

Just east of Dancing Ledge a fault of 80 feet to the west throws back the Purbeck Beds from the cliff edge to well inland and brings up the Portland Sand on the upthrow side. A talus of fallen blocks of stone beneath the cliff indicates the presence of the Sand at sea-level.

The beds then dip gently eastward, past Blacker's Hole, a weak point due to three small faults. They are dropped 25 feet and 12 feet to the west by two more faults, where the Lower Purbeck Broken Beds, Caps, and Dirt Bed may be seen.

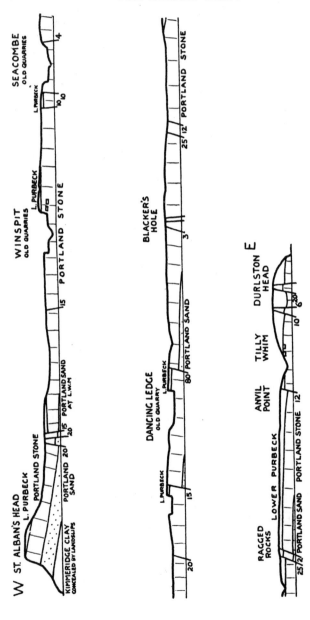

FIG. 29.   THE CLIFFS BETWEEN ST. ALBAN'S HEAD AND DURLSTON HEAD.
Scale : 3 inches to 1 mile horizontally, 6 inches to 1 mile vertically.
The throw of each fault, in feet, is indicated by the figure on the downthrow side.

At the west end of the Ragged Rocks a fault cuts the cliff obliquely. It runs E.N.E. and may be the same fault that is seen in Durlston Head with a downthrow to the north. On the upthrow side the Portland Sand again appears at the foot of the cliff, covered by a talus of fallen blocks, the Ragged Rocks.

Another fault, with a downthrow of 12 feet to the west, occurs south-west of the lighthouse on **Anvil Point.** Beyond the coombe here the old quarry at **Tilly Whim** is seen. The Cherty Series forms the lower part of the cliff and the floor of the quarry, and the Under Freestone was worked by underground galleries,* and lowered into boats moored beneath, as was done at the other quarries on the cliff. In the higher part of the cliff an oyster bed occurs at the horizon of the Blue Stone. It is a mass of shells of *Ostrea expansa, Isognomon (Perna) bouchardi, Exogyra nana,* and *E. thurmanni* From the quarry floor an inclined tunnel leads up to the road.

A group of small faults lies west of **Durlston Head,** and in the Head itself are two more, one with a downthrow of 10 feet to the south, the other 80 feet to the north.

DURLSTON BAY AND PEVERIL POINT.

(1 mile. Six-inch map, Dorset, 57 S.W.)

In Durlston Bay we have the finest section of the Purbeck Beds in England, and here they attain their greatest thickness of 400 feet. They dip north, so that the base is seen at Durlston Head and the Upper Purbeck at Peveril Point; and most of the succession is repeated by a couple of strike-faults which throw the beds down to the south, undoing the work of the dip.

The junction of the Purbeck Beds with the Portland Stone at Durlston Head is not easily accessible, and it is complicated by a number of small faults which give a false appearance of unconformity. The **Soft** and **Hard Caps,** with **Dirt Beds,** are present. A major fault drops them 80 feet to the north, to sea-level. This is followed by a downthrow to the south, indicated by the position of the Cinder Bed in the Middle Purbeck, which is well below Durlston Castle although near the cliff top farther north.

---

* Erroneously described as " elevated sea-caves cut by waves " in an American textbook of geology.

Above the Caps is a limestone breccia representing the **Broken Beds** (p. 88). Then follows a thick mass of pale marls and clays containing irregular masses of gypsum. Bands of limestone with *Cypris purbeckensis* occur near the base, the *Cypris* Freestones. The marls contain not only gypsum, which was formerly quarried, but also pseudomorphs of salt crystals. Both these minerals indicate the evaporation of lagoons filled with sea-water, with precipitation of the dissolved salts. The sodium chloride crystallised, as usual, in hopper-shaped cubes, which grew more rapidly at the edges than at the centres of the faces. These crystals, partly embedded in the mud, were

FIG. 30. DURLSTON BAY AND SWANAGE BAY.
(From a photograph, looking north.)

A. Cinder Bed at sea-level. B. The fault promontory. C. Peveril Point (Upper Purbeck). D. Ballard Point and the Foreland (Upper Chalk), beyond which the Bournemouth cliffs appear (Eocene).

dissolved at the next flood, but they left impressions that were filled by the next layer of sediment, and it is on the under surface of this that the pseudomorphs are seen. Barytes and fluorspar have also been recorded in these beds. The super-saline conditions were unfavourable to molluscan life, though the occasional presence of *Protocardia purbeckensis* in them has caused these beds to be known also as the Cockle Beds. Insects occur at two horizons, apparently blown into the lagoon. They include beetles, butterflies, dragon-flies and locusts. The isopod, *Archæoniscus brodiei,* is found here as well as in higher beds. The Marls with Gypsum bring us to the top of the Lower Purbeck, which is 170 feet thick.

The **Middle Purbeck** starts with a dirt bed, a brown, earthy layer which has yielded at one lucky spot a rich mammalian fauna with *Plagiaulax, Triconodon,* and many other genera. Above it come the **Lower Building Stones,** 34 feet thick. A band of limestone near the middle contains nodules of chert as well as freshwater mollusca. This is known as the Flint Bed (*Plate* VII. B), and below it is a band of dark shale with insects and fish remains. The top course of these Building Stones is the Feather Bed of the quarrymen.

Next comes the most conspicuous bed in the series and one which forms a datum plane throughout the Isle of Purbeck and as far distant as Portisham on the west and the Vale of Wardour on the north. It marks a widespread marine invasion, in which masses of shells of *Ostrea distorta* accumulated to form a grey stone known as the **Cinder Bed.** Occasional shells of *Trigonia, Isognomon,* and *Protocardia* occur, and also the Echinoid, *Hemicidaris purbeckensis,* which seems to be confined to a band near the middle of the Cinder Bed. The bed forms a large scar on the shore a little north of an old quarry in the Lower Building Stone.

Above the Cinder Bed come the **Upper Building Stones,** 50 feet of grey, slabby limestones with shale partings. They have been quarried on the cliff, but much more extensively on the dip-slope to the south-west of Swanage. Together with the Lower Building Stones they have yielded many remains of fish and turtles. Marine shells occur in the White Roach at the top and also at lower levels, separated by beds with fresh-water forms. The shales yield *Cypridea punctata.*

Then follows a series of shelly limestones and shales, well seen above the path that slopes down from Durlston Head. These, the **Corbula Beds,** yield *Corbula alata* and other species, *Modiola, Ostrea,* etc. Layers of "beef" (fibrous calcite) and selenite crystals also occur. The *Corbula* Beds pass up into the **Chief Beef Beds,** dark shales with beef and selenite and with less limestone than the *Corbula* Beds. Together they are 64 feet thick, and they complete the Middle Purbeck, which is here 160 feet thick.

Midway between Durlston Head and Peveril Point the sequence is broken by two faults which bring up the Lower Purbeck again and repeat most of the beds we have passed over. The faults converge to a point on the shore close to the foot of the zig-zag path down from Belle Vue restaurant; one runs west, the other north-west, and the wedge between them forms a projecting bluff. The top of the Building Stones has here reached sea-level, and the Cinder Bed is well below the shore. The first fault brings it up to the lower part of the

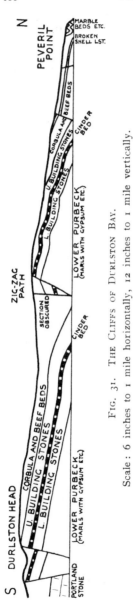

FIG. 31. THE CLIFFS OF DURLSTON BAY.

Scale: 6 inches to 1 mile horizontally, 12 inches to 1 mile vertically.

cliff, the second raises it to the cliff top. It was just north of the faults, in the upper part of the cliff, that Beckles opened the quarry that yielded nearly all the fauna from the Mammal Bed.

Beyond the zig-zag path we find the Lower Purbeck Marls with Gypsum in the cliff for some 300 yards. They are followed by the Mammal Bed, Lower Building Stones, Cinder Bed, Upper Building Stones, *Corbula* and Beef Beds as before. A small fault near Peveril Point has a downthrow of 6 feet to the west.

It is only at **Peveril Point** that the **Upper Purbeck** reaches the shore. It starts with 10 feet of hard limestone made up of comminuted shells of *Cyrena, Unio,* etc., called the **Broken Shell Limestone** or Burr. This is well seen in the cliff and running out in the southern reef at Peveril Point, and it is brought up again by a sharp syncline to form the northern reef.

Above it lie the **Unio Beds, a** thin series of clays and limestones containing *Unio* and also *Cyrena, Viviparus,* and remains of fish, turtles and crocodiles.

More clays and shales follow, with a band of limestone in which *Unio* is more prominent than in the *Unio* Beds, and two bands of **Purbeck Marble,** one red and the other green. This is a freshwater limestone crowded with shells of *Viviparus (Paludina) cariniferus* and *V. elongatus.* These beds are seen in the sharp minor folds within the Peveril Point syncline, and in the reefs.

The highest beds of the Purbeck are not seen at Swanage,

where the junction with the Wealden is masked by Alluvium. They consist of marls with *Viviparus*. The Upper Purbeck is probably 60 or 70 feet thick here.

On the north side of Peveril Point the Broken Shell Limestone forms a platform sloping seaward on the shore below the Grosvenor Hotel. Curious circular depressions in its surface were noted by Fitton in 1836, but are still unexplained.

SWANAGE BAY.

(2 miles. Six-inch maps, Dorset, 57 S.W., 57 N.W.)

From the open space at the end of Victoria Avenue a good view of the Swanage area may be obtained. Northward, Chalk forms the high ground of Ballard Down, with the cliffs from Ballard Point to the Foreland. The fault-gap at Ulwell separates Ballard Down from Nine Barrow Down. Detached sea-stacks lie off the Chalk cliff, and on a clear day one may see the continuation of the Chalk ridge in the western part of the Isle of Wight, where again stacks are developed in the Needles. Farther north, the cliffs of Bournemouth may be seen, with Hengistbury Head to the north-east; these are cut in Middle and Upper Eocene Beds.

Below Ballard Down are narrow outcrops of Upper Greensand, Gault and Lower Greensand, their dip, like that of the southern part of the Chalk, being very high. They reach the coast in what is known as Punfield Cove, though the name does not appear on the Ordnance maps.

The low cliffs from there to Swanage are in Wealden Beds which, having far less resistance than the Chalk above or the Purbeck Beds beneath, have been eroded to a wide valley inland and a bay on the coast. Upper Purbeck Limestones run out to Peveril Point and bound the bay on the south. The dip is still fairly steep, however, and the Upper Purbeck has a narrow outcrop along the line of Swanage High Street and then north of Langton Matravers and Kingston. Along this line the old marble pits were situated. It is the Middle Purbeck that forms the ridge to the south and west of the town, and this ridge is honeycombed with old workings for building stone(*Plate* VI. B).

The total thickness of the **Wealden** in Swanage Bay is estimated at 2,300 feet, but this is based on the width of outcrop and the dip, which varies from 18° to 62°. It may well be an over-estimate. The lower part is hidden beneath the concrete of Beach Road. Where the road turns inland a line of low cliffs begins, partly guarded by a sea wall built to retard the erosion of the unstable cliffs and the destruction of the houses perched above them. A fault south of the Grand Hotel seems to be the same fault that causes the gap at Ulwell and the spring there. On the coast it has a downthrow of only 5 feet to the south-west, and is obscured by slip. Probably it is a tear fault, with more horizontal displacement than vertical.

The cliffs here show green, red and mottled marls, often with lignite, sands and sandstones, and a three-foot band of coarse grit with pebbles of quartz. This may correspond, as Strahan claimed, to the quartz-grit seen at Durdle Door, Lulworth Cove, Mupe Bay and Worbarrow Bay.

Ironstone with *Viviparus*, crystals of selenite, and stumps of trees occur in the beds beyond a little ravine. The cliffs then recede, owing to foundering, and in **Punfield Cove** the highest 35 feet of the Wealden show much shale alternating with sands and bands containing *Viviparus, Cyrena,* and at the top *Ostrea* also.

The **Lower Greensand** is now grassed over at Punfield Cove. It once showed about 50 feet of so-called Atherfield Clay, with a basal pebble bed, followed by 150 feet of sands, ferruginous sandstones and clay. Marine fossils occur; the supposed alternation of freshwater and marine deposits, described by Judd in 1871 as occurring in what he called the " Punfield Beds," was not borne out by later observations.

The **Gault** and **Upper Greensand,** estimated to be about 150 feet thick, are also poorly exposed in this little cove, where coast erosion seems to be very slow at present. They include blue, clayey sand below and green sand above, the latter with lumps of chert in the top 6 feet and abundant *Exogyra conica, Pecten asper, P. orbicularis,* and *Schlœnbachia varians*. Chloritic Marl and Lower Chalk follow.

THE CHALK CLIFFS FROM SWANAGE BAY TO STUDLAND BAY.

(2 miles. Six-inch map, Dorset, 57 N.W.)

Ballard Cliff exceeds 300 feet in height and runs roughly along the strike of the Chalk, which dips north at a high angle, 60° to 90°. The face is masked by scree, but fossils may be collected from the fallen blocks, and in places outcrops of solid rock may be seen running along the shore. Thus outcrops of Upper Greensand and Chloritic Marl may be found

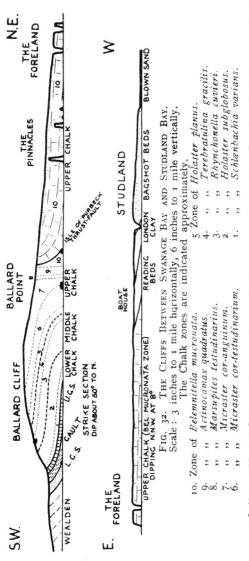

FIG. 32. THE CLIFFS BETWEEN SWANAGE BAY AND STUDLAND BAY.
Scale : 3 inches to 1 mile horizontally, 6 inches to 1 mile vertically.
The Chalk zones are indicated approximately.

10. Zone of *Belemnitella mucronata*.
9. ,, ,, *Actinocamax quadratus*.
8. ,, ,, *Marsupites testudinarius*.
7. ,, ,, *Micraster cor-anguinum*.
6. ,, ,, *Micraster cor-testudinarium*.
5. Zone of *Holaster planus*.
4. ,, ,, *Terebratulina gracilis*.
3. ,, ,, *Rhynchonella cuvieri*.
2. ,, ,, *Holaster subglobosus*.
1. ,, ,, *Schlœnbachia varians*.

on the shore well to eastward of fallen masses of Middle and Upper Chalk.

It is possible at low tide to walk over the upturned edges of the Lower and Middle Chalk, recognising in succession the zones of *Schlœnbachia varians*, *Holaster subglobosus*, *Rhynchonella cuvieri*, and *Terebratulina gracilis*. Farther than this one cannot walk, and the rest of the cliff is best seen from a boat.

At **Ballard Point** the Chalk becomes vertical. The southern side of the Point is in the zone of *Holaster planus*. The cave at the point is partly in yellowish nodular Chalk of the *cortestudinarium* zone, partly in white *coranguinum* Chalk. In the bay beyond is white Chalk with few flints belonging to the *Marsupites* zone, while the zone of *Actinocamax quadratus* (yellowish Chalk with more lines of flints) extends as far as Argyll Point, which

is marked but not named on the six-inch map. The zone of
Belemnitella mucronata comes on before the fault is reached
and forms the whole of the cliffs thence past the Foreland and
into Studland Bay. Its thickness must be at least 250 feet.

About 120 yards north of Ballard Point, the vertical
bedding planes of the Chalk are truncated by a line that
sweeps up in a fine curve from a small cave at the foot of the
cliff to the cliff-top, about 250 feet above sea-level. The Chalk
on the northern side conforms to this line, passing from nearly
vertical to nearly horizontal. This is not a case of unconformity, which it resembles at first sight, but an overthrust

FIG. 33. THE ISLE OF PURBECK THRUST FAULT.
(North of Ballard Point. From a photograph.)
Curved Chalk on the right is thrust southward along
a bedding plane over vertical Chalk on the left.

fault, the Chalk on the north having been pushed over that on
the south. Both are in the zone of *Belemnitella mucronata,*
and this fact alone disposes of the unconformity theory, which
requires a considerable lapse of time unrepresented by sedi-
ments. The flints are badly crushed, and the Chalk below the
thrust is seamed with secondary calcite, while minor cracks
and displacements occur. This is an excellent section of the
Isle of Purbeck thrust fault, which runs westward through
the Chalk and Eocene Beds and cuts the coast again between
White Nothe and Durdle Door (p. 80), where, however, the
section is spoilt by the obliquity with which it cuts the cliff and

the fact that the actual fracture is lost in a belt of shattered Chalk.

Half a mile beyond Ballard Point are the **Pinnacles,** the first a slender detached column of Chalk, the second more elongated in section. Beyond it is the large cave called the Parson's Barn. The horizontal Chalk is traversed by vertical joints, and the sea working along these joints has carved the coast-line into coves, spurs and stacks, which have a somewhat artificial appearance with their dominant straight lines. All stages in the formation of caves, arches and stacks may be observed. The large mass of Chalk forming the **Foreland** or **Handfast Point** was joined to the cliff by a narrow ridge at the beginning of this century. The large stack to the east of it is known as Old Harry, and just north of the latter is all that remains of Old Harry's Wife, which collapsed in 1896.

Beyond the Foreland the coast turns westward, and the Chalk dips at a low angle a little west of north. The cliffs are only 80 feet high, and less toward the west, and there is a fairly wide shelf exposed below them when the tide is out. Some strong springs are thrown out between tide marks. Beyond these springs the Eocene Beds appear at the cliff top and descend to the shore, the Chalk disappearing below sea-level as the coast begins to trend north-westward.

STUDLAND BAY.

(3 miles. Six-inch maps, Dorset, 57 N.W., 51 S.W.)

The Eocene beds south-east of Studland rest on a piped surface of Chalk, *i.e.,* the Chalk has been dissolved irregularly by water descending through the Reading Beds. There is, of course, a great unconformity between the two Series, though no angular discordance can be seen. The abrupt change from a very pure limestone to clays and sands is the only obvious sign here of a lapse of time unrepresented by deposits.

The **Reading Beds** appear at the top of the Chalk cliff about 300 yards east of the angle of Studland Bay, and descend, sloped and covered with bushes, to shore-level at the angle. At their base is a ferruginous grit with rolled flints, and some mottled clay. This is followed by about 40 feet of white sand.

The **London Clay** forms a more gentle slope, often a wet one, from cliff-top to shore. It is a sandy clay, and only about 100 feet thick here.

The remainder of the cliff is in **Bagshot Beds** and shows sands stained vivid shades of red and yellow by ferric oxide, like the corresponding sands of Alum Bay in the Isle of Wight. In places there are cylindrical concretions that weather out from the softer sand and somewhat resemble rusty iron pipes, but a tap from a hammer or the recognition of sand grains embedded in limonite shows their true nature. Near the surface the sands are bleached to a greyish white, the ferric oxide having been reduced and leached out by water that has percolated through decaying vegetable matter.

The cliffs soon turn inland and become degraded, Blown Sand fringing the shore as far as the mouth of Poole Harbour. Captain Diver has shown (1933) how very recent this accretion of land is, the shallow lake known as Little Sea having been a branch of the sea in the Seventeenth Century. The sand is non-calcareous, unlike the Blown Sand of Cornwall and the West Coast, which is largely made up of shell fragments. Hence the marram grass of the youngest dunes is replaced in the older ones by heather, ling, and a calciphobe flora like that of the equally limeless Bagshot Beds.

At the mouth of Poole Harbour rough blocks of stone have been dumped to form a breakwater with the intention of concentrating the tidal scour and using it to keep open a deep channel at the harbour entrance. Beyond the Harbour there is still some three miles of Dorset coast, with Blown Sand, Plateau Gravel and Bagshot Beds, but this stretch belongs naturally to Hampshire, although the county boundary has been drawn between Branksome Chine and Alum Chine.

The Agglestone is worth a visit. It is a mass of ferruginous sandstone which has resisted erosion while the loose sands around it have been swept away. It lies three-quarters of a mile W.N.W. from Studland Church and can be seen from any point on the ridge west of Studland.

The Bagshot Beds of Dorset contain not only sands but gravels and clays. Some of the latter are used for making bricks and tiles; others are sufficiently free from iron to burn to a good white pottery. These are the valuable pipe clays (originally used for making tobacco pipes) and ball clays, so called because they were dug out in blocks or balls about nine inches across. They are highly plastic clays and can be added to kaolin to impart plasticity to it. Lignite and finely divided vegetable matter are associated with the clays. Well-preserved leaves occur in some of the beds, but they are seldom seen now that the workings are largely underground. The ball clays have been worked for two hundred years around Poole Harbour.

V. A SELECTED LIST OF BOOKS AND PAPERS ON THE GEOLOGY OF DORSET*

ALLEN, T. D., 1863, "The Portland Fissures with Human Remains." *Geologist*, vol. VI., pp. 209, 296. (See also pp. 94, 136, 251.)

ANDERSON, F. W., 1932, "Phasal Deposition in the Middle Purbeck Beds of Dorset." *Rep. Brit. Assoc.*, London, 1931, p. 379.

ARKELL, W. J., 1929, "A Monograph of British Corallian Lamellibranchia." *Pal. Soc.*

——, 1930, "A Comparison between the Jurassic Rocks of the Calvados Coast and those of Southern England." *Proc. Geol. Assoc.*, vol. XLI., p. 396.

——, 1932, "An Unknown Kellaways Locality in Dorset." *Geol. Mag.*, p. 44.

——, 1933, "The Jurassic System in Great Britain." Oxford.

——, 1934, "Report of Field Meeting in the Isle of Purbeck." *Proc. Geol. Assoc.*, vol. XLV., p. 412.

——, 1935, "The Portland Beds of the Dorset Mainland." *Proc. Geol. Assoc.*, vol. XLVI.

AUSTEN, J. H., 1852, "A Guide to the Geology of the Isle of Purbeck and the South-West Coast of Hampshire." 8vo. Blandford.

BADEN-POWELL, D., 1930, "On the Geological Evolution of the Chesil Bank." *Geol. Mag.*, p. 499.

BARRETT, C., 1878, "The Geology of Swyre, Puncknowle, Burton Bradstock, Loders, Shipton Gorge, Litton Cheney, Longbredy, Littlebredy and Abbotsbury, Dorset." 8vo. Bridport.

BARROIS, C., 1876, "Recherches sur le Terrain Crétacé Supérieur de l'Angleterre et de l'Irlande." *Mém. Soc. Géol. Nord.*

BLACK, W. J., 1878, "Remarks on the Chesil Bank." *Trans. Manch. Geol. Soc.*, vol. XV., p. 43, and *Proc. Roy. Phys. Soc., Edinburgh*, vol. IV., p. 123.

BLAKE, J. F., 1875, "On the Kimmeridge Clay of England." *Quart. Journ. Geol. Soc.*, vol. XXXI., p. 196.

——, 1880, "On the Portland Rocks of England." *Quart. Journ. Geol. Soc.*, vol. XXXVI., p. 189.

——, 1905-07, "A Monograph of the Fauna of the Cornbrash." *Pal. Soc.*

—— and HUDLESTON, W. H., 1877, "On the Corallian Rocks of England." *Quart. Journ. Geol. Soc.*, vol. XXXIII., p. 260.

—— ——, 1879, "Excursion to Weymouth and Portland." *Proc. Geol. Assoc.*, vol. VI., p. 172.

——, ——, and BUCKMAN, S. S., 1898, "Excursion to Bridport and Weymouth." *Proc. Geol. Assoc.*, vol. XV., p. 293.

BOSWELL, P. G. H., 1924, "The Petrography of the Sands of the Upper Lias and Lower Inferior Oolite in the West of England." *Geol. Mag.*, p. 246.

——, 1929, (1) "Cretaceous System." In Evans and Stubblefield, *Handbook of the Geology of Great Britain*, p. 383.

——, 1929, (2), "Tertiary Group." In Evans and Stubblefield, *Handbook of the Geology of Great Britain*, p. 411.

BOTT, T. D., "Geology of the Neighbourhood of Swanage." *Proc. Geol. Assoc.*, vol. II., p. 30.

* See also supplementary list on page 123.

BRISTOW, H. W., and WHITAKER, W., 1869, " On the Formation of the Chesil Bank, Dorset." *Geol. Mag.,* p. 433. (See also pp. 325, 574.)

BRODIE, P. B., 1854, " On the Insect Beds of the Purbeck Formation in Wiltshire and Dorsetshire." *Quart. Journ. Geol. Soc.,* vol. X, p. 475.

BRODIE, W. R., 1876, " Notes on the Kimmeridge Clay of the Isle of Purbeck." *Proc. Geol. Assoc.,* vol. IV., p. 517.

BUCKLAND, W., 1835, " On the Discovery of Fossil Bones of the Iguanodon, in the Iron Sand of the Wealden Formation in the Isle of Wight, and in the Isle of Purbeck." *Trans. Geol. Soc.,* Series II., vol. III., part III., p. 425.

——, and DE LA BECHE, H. T., 1835, " On the Geology of the Neighbourhood of Weymouth and the Adjacent Parts of the Coast of Dorset." *Trans. Geol. Soc.,* Series II., vol IV., p. 1.

BUCKMAN, J., 1866, " On the Geology of the County of Dorset in reference to Agriculture and Rural Economy." *Journ. Bath and W. England Agric. Soc.,* New Series, vol. XIV., p. 36.

——, 1873, " On the Cephalopoda-bed and the Oolite Sands of Dorset and part of Somerset." *Quart. Journ. Geol. Soc.,* vol. XXIX., p. 504 (abstract); *Proc. Somerset Arch. Lit. Soc.,* vol. XX., p. 140. 1875. (Printed in full.)

——, 1877, (1) " The Cephalopoda-beds of Gloucester, Dorset and Somerset." *Quart. Journ. Geol. Soc.,* vol. XXXIII., p. 1.

——, 1877, (2) " On the Fossil Beds of Bradford Abbas and its Vicinity." *Proc. Dorset Nat. Hist. Club,* vol. I., p. 64.

——, 1878, " On some slabs of Trigonia clavellata, from Osmington Mills, Dorset." *Proc. Dorset Field Club,* vol. II., p. 19.

——, 1879, " On the so-called Midford Sands." *Quart. Journ. Geol. Soc.,* vol. XXXV., p. 736.

BUCKMAN, S. S., 1878, " On the species of Astarte from the Inferior Oolite of the Sherborne District." *Proc. Dorset Field Club,* vol. II., p. 81.

——, 1889, " On the Cotteswold, Midford and Yeovil Sands and the Division between Lias and Oolite." *Quart. Journ. Geol. Soc.,* vol. XLV., p. 440.

——, 1890, " On the so-called ' Upper Lias Clay ' of Down Cliffs." *Quart. Journ. Geol. Soc.,* vol. XLVI., p. 518.

——, 1891, " The Ammonite Zones of Dorset and Somerset." *Geol. Mag.,* p. 502.

——, 1893, (1) " The Bajocian of the Sherborne District : its Relation to Subjacent and Superjacent Strata." *Quart. Journ. Geol. Soc.,* vol. XLIX., p. 479.

——, 1893, (2) " ' The Top of the Inferior Oolite ' and a Correlation of ' Inferior Oolite ' Deposits." *Proc. Dorset Field Club,* vol. XIV., p. 37.

——, 1898, " On the Grouping of some Divisions of so-called ' Jurassic ' Time." *Quart. Journ. Geol. Soc.,* vol. LIV., p. 442.

——, 1902, " The Term ' Hemera.' " *Geol. Mag.,* p. 554.

——, 1909-30, " Type Ammonites."

——, 1910, " Certain Jurassic (Lias-Oolite) Strata of South Dorset and their Correlation." *Quart. Journ. Geol. Soc.,* vol. LXVI., p. 52.

——, 1918, " Jurassic Chronology : I.—Lias." *Quart. Journ. Geol. Soc.,* vol. LXXIII., p. 257.

——, 1922, " Jurassic Chronology : II.—Preliminary Studies. Certain Jurassic Strata near Eypesmouth (Dorset); the Junction-Bed of Watton Cliff and Associated Rocks." *Quart. Journ. Geol. Soc.,* vol. LXXVIII., p. 378.

BUCKMAN, S. S., 1927, " Jurassic Chronology : III.—Some Faunal Horizons in Cornbrash." *Quart. Journ. Geol. Soc.,* vol. LXXXIII., p. 1.

BURTON, E. ST. J., 1932, " A Peneplain and Re-excavated Valley Floors in Dorsetshire." *Geol. Mag.,* p. 474.

CAMERON, A. C. G., 1909, " On a Well-section at Ware House, near Lyme Regis, and the Fossils obtained therefrom." *Geol. Mag.,* p. 169.

——, 1913, " The Geology of Lyme Regis."

CASLEY, G., 1880, " Geology of Lyme Regis." 8vo., Lyme Regis (two later editions).

CHAPMAN, F., 1906, " Note on an Ostracodal Limestone from Durlston Bay," *Proc. Geol. Assoc.,* vol. XIX., p. 283.

CHATWIN, C. P., 1932, " The Dorset Coast, near Weymouth." *Proc. Geol. Assoc.,* vol. XLIII., p. 277.

CLARKE, W. B., 1837, " Illustrations of the Geology of the South-East of Dorsetshire. No. 1. The Vertical and Curved Chalk Strata of Ballard Head, near Swanwich." *Mag. Nat. Hist.,* vol. X., pp. 414, 461.

——, 1838, (1) " Illustrations of the Geology of the South-East of Dorsetshire. No. 2. On the Strata between Durlstone Head and Old Harry Rocks." *Mag. Nat. Hist.,* Series II., vol. II., pp. 79, 128.

——, 1838, (2) " On the Peat Bogs and Submarine Forests of Bourne Mouth, Hampshire, and in the Neighbourhood of Poole, Dorsetshire." *Proc. Geol. Soc.,* vol. II., p. 599.

——, 1839, " Illustrations of the Geology of the South-East of Dorsetshire. No. 3. Studland." *Mag. Nat. Hist.,* Series II., vol. III., pp. 390, 435, 483.

CODRINGTON, T., 1870, " Some Remarks on the Formation of the Chesil Bank." *Geol. Mag.,* p. 23.

CONYBEARE, W. D., 1840, " Extraordinary Landslip and great Convulsion of the Coast of Culverhole Point, near Axmouth." *Edin. New Phil. Journ.,* vol. XXIX., p. 160.

—— and others, 1840, " Ten Plates, comprising a Plan, Sections and Views, Representing the Changes Produced on the Coast of East Devon, between Axmouth and Lyme Regis, by the Subsidence of the Land and Elevation of the Bottom of the Sea, on December 26th, 1839, and February 3rd, 1840." London.

COODE, J., 1853, " Description of the Chesil Bank, with remarks upon its Origin, the Causes which have contributed to its Formation, and upon the Movement of Shingle generally." *Proc. Inst. Civ. Eng.,* vol. XII., p. 520.

CORNISH, VAUGHAN, 1898, " On Sea-Beaches and Sandbanks. §11. On the Chesil Bank, a Local Study in the Grading of Beach Shingle." *Geog. Journ.,* vol. XI., p. 628.

DAMON, R., 1860, " Geology of Weymouth and the Island of Portland. With Supplement containing Plates of the Fossils." Stanford, London (two later editions).

DAVIES, A. M., 1929, " Jurassic System." In Evans and Stubblefield, *Handbook of the Geology of Great Britain,* p. 350.

DAY, E. C. H., 1863, " On the Middle and Upper Lias of the Dorsetshire Coast." *Quart. Journ. Geol. Soc.,* vol. XIX., p. 278.

——, 1865, " On the Lower Lias of Lyme Regis." *Geol. Mag.,* p. 518.

DE LA BECHE, H. T., 1822, " Remarks on the Geology of the South Coast of England, from Bridport Harbour, Dorset, to Babbacombe Bay, Devon." *Trans. Geol. Soc.,* Series II., vol. I., p. 40.

——, 1826, (1) " On the Lias of the Coast, in the Vicinity of Lyme Regis, Dorset." *Trans. Geol. Soc.,* Series II., vol. II., p. 21.

DE LA BECHE, H. T., 1826, (2) "On the Chalk and Sands beneath it (usually termed Green-sand) in the vicinity of Lyme Regis, Dorset, and Beer, Devon." *Trans. Geol. Soc.*, Series II., vol. II., p. 109.

——, 1826, (3) "Notice of Traces of a Submarine Forest at Charmouth, Dorset." *Ann. Phil.*, Series II., vol. XI., p. 143.

DE RANCE, C. E., 1874, "On the Physical Changes preceding the Deposition of the Cretaceous Strata in the South-West of England." *Geol. Mag.*, p. 246.

DIVER, C., 1933, "The Physiography of the South Haven Peninsula, Studland Heath." *Geog. Jnl.*, vol. LXXXI., p. 404.

DOUGLAS, J. A., and ARKELL, W. J.,. 1928, "The Stratigraphical Distribution of the Cornbrash. I. The South-Western Area." *Quart. Journ. Geol. Soc.*, vol. LXXXIV., p. 117.

DOWNES, W., 1885, "The Cretaceous Beds at Black Ven, near Lyme Regis, with some Supplementary Remarks on the Blackdown Beds." *Quart. Journ. Geol. Soc.*, vol. XLI., p. 23.

EDMUNDS, F. H., and SCHAFFER, R. J., 1932, "Portland Stone : its Geology and Properties as a Building Stone." *Proc. Geol. Assoc.*, vol. XLIII., p. 225.

FISHER, O., 1856, "On the Purbeck Strata of Dorsetshire." *Trans. Cambridge Phil. Soc.*, vol. IX., p. 555.

——, 1859, "On some Natural Pits on the Heaths of Dorsetshire." *Quart. Journ. Geol. Soc.*, vol. XV., p. 187.

——, 1861, "Fissures in Portland Strata." *Geologist*, vol. IV., p. 556.

——, 1863, "The Portland Ossiferous Fissures." *Geologist*, vol. VI., p. 250.

——, 1873, "On the Origin of the Estuary of the Fleet in Dorsetshire." *Geol. Mag.*, pp. 481, 573.

——, 1874, Letter on the origin of the Estuary of the Fleet. *Geol. Mag.*, p. 190.

——, 1874, Letter on the Chesil Bank. *Geol. Mag.*, p. 285.

——, 1877, "*Elephas meridionalis* in Dorset." *Geol. Mag.*, p. 527.

——, 1886, "Memorandum for Geologists visiting Weymouth." *Geol. Mag.*, p. 336.

——, 1888, "On the Occurrence of *Elephas meridionalis* at Dewlish, Dorset." *Quart. Journ. Geol. Soc.*, vol. XLIV., p. 818.

——, 1896, "Vertical Tertiaries at Bincombe, Dorset." *Geol. Mag.*, p. 246.

——, 1905, "On the Occurrence of *Elephas meridionalis* at Dewlish, Dorset. Second Communication ; Human Agency Suggested." *Quart. Journ. Geol. Soc.*, vol. LXI., p. 35.

FITTON, W. H., 1835, "Notice on the Junction of the Portland and the Purbeck Strata on the Coast of Dorsetshire." *Proc. Geol. Soc.*, vol. II., p. 185.

——, 1836, "Observations on some of the Strata between the Chalk and the Oxford Oolite in the South-East of England." *Trans. Geol. Soc.*, Series II., vol. IV., p. 103.

FORDHAM, H. G., 1876, "On the Section of the Chloritic Marl and Upper Greensand on the Northern Side of Swanage Bay." *Proc. Geol. Assoc.*, vol. IV., p. 506.

FOX, W., 1862, "When and how was the Isle of Wight separated from the Mainland?" *Geologist*, vol. V., p. 452.

GARDNER, J. S., 1878, "On the Lower Bagshot Beds of the Hampshire Basin." *Proc. Geol. Assoc.*, vol. V., p. 51.

——, 1894, "Excursion to Bournemouth and Barton " [Swanage included]. *Proc. Geol. Assoc.*, vol. XIII., p. 276.

GODWIN-AUSTEN, R. A. C., 1850, "On the Valley of the English Channel." *Quart. Journ. Geol. Soc.*, vol. VI., p. 69.

GRAY, W., 1861, "On the Geology of the Isle of Portland." *Proc. Geol. Assoc.*, vol. I., p. 128.

GREEN, B., 1886, "Kimmeridge Shale : its Origin, History, and Uses." 8vo. London.

GREENWOOD, G., 1869, "On the Formation of the Chesil Bank." *Geol. Mag.*, p. 523.

——, 1874, (1) Letter on the Origin of the Fleet. *Geol. Mag.*, p. 143.

——, 1874, (2) "Why are the largest stones found at the East End of the Chesil Bank?" *Geol. Mag.*, p. 576.

GROVES, T. B., 1875, "The Chesil Bank." *Nature*, vol. XI., p. 506.

——, 1887, "The Abbotsbury Iron Deposits." *Proc. Dorset Field Club*, vol. VIII., p. 64.

——, 1889, "Erosion of Coast near Weymouth." *Proc. Dorset Field Club*, vol. X., p. 180.

HOLL, H. B., 1863, "On the Correlation of the several Subdivisions of the Inferior Oolite in the Middle and South of England." *Quart. Journ. Geol. Soc.*, vol. XIX., p. 306.

HOLMES, T. V., 1884, "On Some Curious Excavations in the Isle of Portland." *Proc. Geol. Assoc.*, vol. VIII., p. 404.

HOVENDEN, F., MONCKTON, H. W., ORD, W. T., and SMITH WOODWARD, A., 1910, "Excursion to Swanage, Lulworth Cove and Bournemouth." *Proc. Geol. Assoc.*, vol. XXI., p. 510.

HUDLESTON, W. H., 1882, "Excursion to the Isle of Purbeck." *Proc. Geol. Assoc.*, vol. VII., p. 377.

——, 1885, "Excursion to Sherborne and Bridport." *Proc. Geol. Assoc.*, vol. IX., p. 187.

——, 1889, "Excursion to Weymouth." *Proc. Geol. Assoc.*, vol. XI., p. xlix.

——, 1902, "Creechbarrow in Purbeck." *Geol. Mag.*, p. 241.

——, 1903, "Creechbarrow in Purbeck.—No. 2." *Geol. Mag.*, pp. 149, 197.

——, 1910, "Dorset—Inland." In "Geology in the Field : the Jubilee Volume of the Geologists' Association," Part II., p. 365.

——, MANSEL, O. L., and MONCKTON, H. W., 1896, "Excursion to Swanage, Corfe Castle, Kimmeridge, etc." *Proc. Geol. Assoc.*, vol. XIV., p. 307.

——, and WOODWARD, H. B., 1885, "Excursion to Sherborne and Bridport." *Proc. Geol. Assoc.*, vol. IX., p. 187.

JACKSON, J. F., 1922, "Sections of the Junction Bed and Contiguous Deposits." *Quart. Journ. Geol. Soc.*, vol. LXXVIII., p. 436.

——, 1926, "The Junction-Bed of the Middle and Upper Lias on the Dorset Coast." *Quart. Journ. Geol. Soc.*, vol. LXXXII., p. 490.

JUDD, J. W., 1871, "On the Punfield Formation." *Quart. Journ. Geol. Soc.*, vol. XXVII., p. 207.

JUKES-BROWNE, A. J., 1879, "Chloritic Marl and Upper Greensand." *Geol. Mag.*, pp. 47, 143.

——, 1891, "Note on an Undescribed Area of Lower Greensand or Vectian in Dorset." *Geol. Mag.*, p. 456.

——, 1895, "The Origin of the Valleys in the Chalk Downs of North Dorset." *Proc. Dorset Field Club*, vol. XVI., p. 5.

——, 1898, "The Origin of the Vale of Marshwood and of the Greensand Hills of West Dorset." *Geol. Mag.*, p. 161.

——, 1900, "The Cretaceous Rocks of Britain. Vol. I. The Gault and Upper Greensand of England." *Mem. Geol. Survey.*

JUKES-BROWNE, A. J., 1902, "On a Deep Boring at Lyme Regis."
Quart. Journ. Geol. Soc., vol. LVIII., p. 279.

——, 1903, "The Cretaceous Rocks of Britain. Vol. II. The Lower and
Middle Chalk of England." *Mem. Geol. Survey.*

——, 1904, "The Cretaceous Rocks of Britain. Vol. III. The Upper
Chalk of England." *Mem. Geol. Survey.*

——, 1908, "The Burning Cliff and the Landslip at Lyme Regis."
Proc. Dorset Nat. Hist. Field Club, vol. XXIX., p. 153.

KEEPING, H., 1910, "On the Discovery of Bembridge Limestone Fossils
on Creechbarrow Hill, Isle of Purbeck." *Geol. Mag.*, p. 436.

KINAHAN, G. H., 1874, "On the Origin of the Lagoon, called The Fleet,
Dorsetshire." *Geol. Mag.*, p. 50. (See also pp. 189, 239, 240.)

——, 1877, "On the Chesil Beach, Dorsetshire, and Cahore Shingle
Beach, County Wexford." *Quart. Journ. Geol. Soc.*, vol. XXXIII.,
p. 29.

KINGSLEY, C., 1858, Letter on the Haggerstone. *Geologist,* vol. I., p. 75.

KITCHIN, F. L., and PRINGLE, J., 1922, "On the Overlap of the Upper
Gault in England. . . .' *Geol. Mag.*, p. 156.

LAMPLUGH, G. W., WEDD, C. B., and PRINGLE, J., 1920, "Special Re-
ports on the Mineral Resources of Great Britain. Vol. XII.
Bedded Iron Ores of the Lias, Oolites and later Formations in
England." *Mem. Geol. Survey.*

LANG, W. D., 1903, "On a Fossiliferous Bed in the Selbornian of
Charmouth." *Geol. Mag.*, p. 388.

——, 1904, "The Zone of *Hoplites interruptus* (Bruguière) at Black
Ven, Charmouth." *Geol. Mag.*, p. 124.

——, 1907, "The Selbornian of Stonebarrow Cliff, Charmouth." *Geol.
Mag.*, p. 150.

——, 1909, "The Burning Cliff near Lyme Regis." *Geol. Mag.*, p. 89.

——, 1913, "The Lower Pliensbachian—Carixian—of Charmouth."
Geol. Mag., p. 401.

——, 1914, "The Geology of the Charmouth Cliffs, Beach and Fore-
Shore." *Proc. Geol. Assoc.*, vol. XXV., p. 293.

——, 1917, "The Ibex-Zone at Charmouth and its Relation to the
Zones near it." *Proc. Geol. Assoc.*, vol. XXVIII., p. 31.

——, 1924, "The Blue Lias of the Devon and Dorset Coasts." *Proc.
Geol. Assoc.*, vol. XXXV., p. 169.

——, 1926, "The Submerged Forest at the mouth of the River Char
and the History of that River." *Proc. Geol. Assoc.*, vol XXXVII.,
p. 197.

——, 1932, "The Lower Lias of Charmouth and the Vale of Marshwood." *Proc. Geol. Assoc.*, vol. XLIII., p. 97.

——, and SPATH, L. F., 1926, "The Black Marl of Black Ven and Stonebarrow, in the Lias of the Dorset Coast." *Quart. Journ. Geol. Soc.*,
vol. LXXXII., p. 144.

——, ——, COX, L. R., and MUIR-WOOD, H. M., 1928, "The Belemnite
Marls of Charmouth, a Series in the Lias of the Dorset Coast."
Quart. Journ. Geol. Soc., vol. LXXXIV., p. 179.

——, ——, and RICHARDSON, W. A., 1923, "Shales-with-' Beef,' a
Sequence in the Lower Lias of the Dorset Coast." *Quart. Journ.
Geol. Soc.*, vol. LXXIX., p. 47.

LATTER, M. P., 1926, "The Petrography of the Portland Sand of Dorset." *Proc. Geol. Assoc.*, vol. XXXVII., p. 73.

LOBLEY, J. L., 1872, "Excursion to the Yeovil District." *Proc. Geol
Assoc.*, vol. II., p. 247.

LYELL, C., 1827, " On the Strata of the Plastic Clay Formation exhibited in the Cliffs between Christchurch Head, Hampshire, and Studland Bay, Dorsetshire." *Trans. Geol. Soc.,* Series II., vol. II., p. 279.

MANSEL-PLEYDELL, J. C., 1873, " A brief Memoir on the Geology of Dorset." *Geol. Mag.,* pp. 402, 438.

——, 1892, " Kimmeridge Coal-Money and other Manufactured Articles from the Kimmeridge Shale." *Proc. Dorset Field Club,* vol. XIII., p. 178.

——, 1893, " A further note on the Dewlish ' Elephant Bed.' " *Proc. Dorset Field Club,* vol. XIV., p. 139.

——, 1894, " Kimmeridge Shale." *Proc. Dorset Field Club,* vol. XV., p. 172.

MANTELL, G. A., 1847, " Geological Excursions round the Isle of Wight and along the adjacent Coast of Dorsetshire " (two later editions).

MAW, G., 1867, " On the Sources of the Materials composing the White Clays of the Lower Tertiaries." *Quart. Journ. Geol. Soc.,* vol. XXIII., p. 387.

——, 1870, " On Insect Remains and Shells from the Lower Bagshot Leaf-bed of Studland Bay, Dorsetshire." *Rep. Brit. Assoc.* for 1869. Trans. of Sections, p. 97.

MEYER, C. J. A., 1866, " Notes on the Correlation of the Cretaceous Rocks of the South-East and West of England." *Geol. Mag.,* p. 13.

——, 1872, " On the Wealden as a Fluvio-lacustrine Formation, and on the Relations of the so-called ' Punfield Formation ' to the Wealden." *Quart. Journ. Geol. Soc.,* vol. XXVIII., p. 243.

——, 1873, " Further Notes on the Punfield Section." *Quart. Journ. Geol. Soc.,* vol. XXIX., p. 70.

——, 1879, " Chloritic Marl and Upper Greensand." *Geol. Mag.,* p. 143.

MITCHELL, J., 1837, " On the Strata near Swanwich in the Isle of Purbeck." *Mag. Nat. Hist.,* vol. X., p. 587.

MONCKTON, H. W., 1910, " The Dorset Coast." In " Geology in the Field : the Jubilee Volume of the Geologists' Association," Part II., p. 382.

NEALE, A., 1852, " Notice of Fossil Bones at Portland." *Quart. Journ. Geol. Soc.,* vol. VIII., p. 109.

NEAVERSON, E., 1925, " The Petrography of the Upper Kimmeridge Clay and Portland Sand in Dorset, Wiltshire, Oxfordshire and Buckinghamshire." *Proc. Geol. Assoc.,* vol. XXXVI., p. 240.

OPPEL, A., 1856-58, " Die Juraformation Englands, Frankreichs und des südwestlichen Deutschlands."

ORD, W. T., and RICHARDSON, L., 1914, " Excursion to Weymouth, Portland, Wool, Wareham, Corfe, Lulworth and Dorchester." *Proc. Cotteswold Nat. Field Club,* vol. XVIII., p. 218.

PAVLOW, A. P., 1896, " On the Classification of the Strata between the Kimmeridgian and Aptian." *Quart. Journ. Geol. Soc.,* vol. LII., p. 542.

PENGELLY, W., 1870, " The Modern and Ancient Beaches of Portland." *Trans. Devon Assoc.,* vol. IV., p. 195.

PRESTWICH, J., 1858, Reply to the letter of the Rev. C. Kingsley on the " Haggerstone." *Geologist,* vol. I., p. 113.

——, 1875, (1) " Notes on the Phenomena of the Quaternary Period in the Isle of Portland and around Weymouth." *Quart. Journ. Geol. Soc.,* vol. XXXI., p. 29.

PRESTWICH, J., 1875, (2) " On the Origin of the Chesil Bank, and on the Relation of the existing Beaches to past Geological Changes independent of the present Coast Action." *Proc. Inst. Civil Eng.*, vol. XL., p. 61.

——, 1892, " The Raised Beaches and ' Head ' or Rubble-Drift of the South of England." *Quart. Journ. Geol. Soc.*, vol. XLVIII., p. 263.

READE, T. M., 1873, " The Chesil Bank." *Geol. Mag.*, p. 573.

——, 1874, " Why are the largest stones found at the East end of the Chesil Bank?" *Geol. Mag.*, p. 286.

REID, C., 1896, " The Eocene Deposits of Dorset." *Quart. Journ. Geol. Soc.*, vol. LII., p. 490.

——, 1898, " The Geology of the Country around Bournemouth." *Mem. Geol. Survey.*

——, 1899, " Geology of the Country around Dorchester." *Mem. Geol. Survey.*

REYNOLDS, S. H., 1926, " The Isle of Purbeck." *Geogr. Teacher,* vol. XIII., p. 433.

RICHARDSON, L., 1906, " On the Rhætic and Contiguous Deposits of Devon and Dorset." *Proc. Geol. Assoc.*, vol. XIX., p. 401.

——, 1909, " The Dorset and Hampshire Coasts, with particular reference to the Forest Marble Beds near Langton Herring." *Proc. Cotteswold Nat. Field Club*, vol. XVI., p. 267.

——, 1913, " Excursion to the Sherborne District, Dorset." *Proc. Cotteswold Nat. Field Club*, vol. XVIII., p. 111.

——, 1915, " Report of an Excursion to Bridport, Beaminster and Crewkerne." *Proc. Geol. Assoc.*, vol. XXVI., p. 47.

——, 1928, -29, -30, " The Inferior Oolite and Contiguous Deposits of the Burton Bradstock-Broadwindsor District, Dorset." *Proc. Cotteswold Nat. Field Club*, vol. XXIII., pp. 35, 149, 253.

——, 1929, " Rhætic." In Evans and Stubblefield, " Handbook of the Geology of Great Britain," p. 341.

——, 1932, " The Inferior Oolite and Contiguous Deposits of the Sherborne District, Dorset." *Proc. Cotteswold Nat. Field Club*, vol. XXIV., p. 35.

——, and RIDDELSDELL, H. J., 1912, " Excursion to Bridport, Dorset." *Proc. Cotteswold Nat. Field Club*, vol. XVIII., p. 31.

ROBERTS, G., 1840, " An Account of, and Guide to, the Mighty Landslip of Dowlands and Bindon, in the Parish of Axmouth, near Lyme Regis, December 25th, 1839." Lyme Regis (and later editions).

ROBERTS, T., 1887, " On the Correlation of the Upper Jurassic Rocks of the Swiss Jura with those of England." *Quart. Journ. Geol. Soc.*, vol. XLIII., p. 229.

ROWE, A. W., 1901, " The Zones of the White Chalk of the English Coast. II.—Dorset." *Proc. Geol. Assoc.*, vol. XVII., p. 1.

SALFELD, H., 1913, " Certain Upper Jurassic Strata of England." *Quart. Journ. Geol. Soc.*, vol. LXIX., p. 423.

SALMON, A. L., 1915, " Dorset." Cambridge County Geographies.

SCOTT, A., 1929, " Special Reports on the Mineral Resources of Great Britain, vol. XXXI., Ball Clays." *Mem. Geol. Survey.*

SOLLY, H. S., and WALKER, J. F., 1890, (1) " The Geology of Bridport." *Proc. Dorset Field Club*, vol. XI., p. 109.

——, ——, 1890, (2) " Note on the Fault in the Cliff West of Bridport Harbour." *Proc. Dorset Field Club*, vol. XI., p. 118.

SPATH, L. F., 1923, " On the Ammonite Horizons of the Gault and Contiguous Deposits." *Summ. Prog. Geol. Survey* for 1922, p. 139.

Spath, L. F., 1924, " The Ammonites of the Blue Lias." *Proc. Geol. Assoc.,* vol. XXXV., p. 186.

——, 1926, (1) " On new Ammonites from the English Chalk." *Geol. Mag.,* p. 77.

——, 1926, (2) " On the Zones of the Cenomanian and the Uppermost Albian." *Proc. Geol. Assoc.,* vol. XXXVII., p. 420.

——, 1931, " On the Contemporaneity of certain Ammonite Beds in England and France." *Geol. Mag.,* p. 182.

Stoddart, W. W., 1871, " Notes on the Geology of Weymouth." *Proc. Bristol Nat. Soc.,* Series II., vol. V., p. 66.

Strahan, A., 1895, " On Overthrusts of Tertiary Date in Dorset." *Quart. Journ. Geol. Soc.,* vol. LI., p. 549.

——, 1896, (1) " Eocene Beds at Bincombe, Dorset." *Geol. Mag.* p. 334.

——, 1896, (2) " The Physical Geology of Purbeck." *Proc. Geol. Assoc.,* vol. XIV., p. 405.

——, 1898, " The Geology of the Isle of Purbeck and Weymouth." *Mem. Geol. Survey.*

——, 1906, " Guide to the Geological Model of the Isle of Purbeck." *Mem. Geol. Survey.*

——, and Pringle, J., 1918, " Special Reports on the Mineral Resources of Great Britain. Vol. VII. Lignites, Jets, Kimmeridge Oil-shale, Mineral Oil, Cannel Coals, Natural Gas. Part I.—England and Wales." *Mem. Geol. Survey.*

Struckmann, C., 1881, " On the Parallelism of the Hanoverian and English Upper Jurassic Formations." *Geol. Mag.,* p. 546.

Stuart, M. G., 1889, " The Ridgway Fault." *Proc. Dorset Field Club,* vol. X., p. 55.

Tarr, W. A., 1933, " Origin of the ' Beef ' in the Lias Shales of the Dorset Coast." *Geol. Mag.,* p. 289.

Walker, J. F., 1892, " On Liassic Sections near Bridport, Dorsetshire." *Geol. Mag.,* p. 437.

Wallis, A. M., 1891, " The Portland Stone Quarries." *Proc. Dorset Field Club,* vol. XII., p. 187.

Webster, T., 1826, " Observations on the Purbeck and Portland Beds." *Trans. Geol. Soc.,* Series II., vol. II., p. 37.

Weston, C. H., 1848, " On the Geology of Ridgway, near Weymouth." *Quart. Journ. Geol. Soc.,* vol. IV., p. 245.

——, 1849, " Further Observations on the Geology of Ridgway, near Weymouth." *Quart. Journ. Geol. Soc.,* vol. V., p. 317.

——, 1852, " On the Sub-escarpments of the Ridgway Range, and their Contemporaneous Deposits in the Isle of Portland." *Quart. Journ. Geol. Soc.,* vol. VIII., p. 110.

Westwood, J. O., 1854, " Contributions to Fossil Entomology." *Quart. Journ. Geol. Soc.,* vol. X., p. 378.

Whitaker, W., 1869, " On a Raised Beach at Portland Bill, Dorset." *Geol. Mag.,* p. 438 (also p. 326).

——, 1871, " On the Chalk of the Southern Part of Dorset and Devon." *Quart. Journ. Geol. Soc.,* vol. XXVII., p. 93.

White, H. J. O., 1917, " Geology of the Country around Bournemouth." Second Edition. *Mem. Geol. Survey.*

Willett, E. W., and H., 1881, " Notes on a Mammalian Jaw from the Purbeck Beds at Swanage, Dorset." *Quart. Journ. Geol. Soc.,* vol. XXXVII., p. 376.

Wilson, E., 1870, " Notes on the Fleet and Chesil Bank." *Geol. Mag.,* p. 140.

WOOD, H. H., 1877, "Notes on some Cornbrash Sections in Dorset." *Proc. Dorset Field Club*, vol. I., p. 22.

WOODWARD, H. B., 1885, "Excursion to Bridport, Bothenhampton, Burton Bradstock, Bridport Harbour and Eype." *Proc. Geol. Assoc.*, vol. IX., p. 200.

——, 1888, "The Relations of the Great Oolite to the Forest Marble and Fuller's Earth in the South-West of England." *Geol. Mag.*, p. 467.

——, 1889, "Preliminary Excursion to Lyme Regis." *Proc. Geol. Assoc.*, vol. XI., p. xxvi.

——, 1892, "The Geology of Swanage." 8vo.

——, 1893, "The Jurassic Rocks of Britain. Vol. III. The Lias of England and Wales (Yorkshire excepted)." *Mem. Geol. Survey.*

——, 1894, "The Jurassic Rocks of Britain. Vol. IV. The Lower Oolitic Rocks of England (Yorkshire excepted)." *Mem. Geol. Survey.*

——, 1895, "The Jurassic Rocks of Britain. Vol. V. The Middle and Upper Oolitic Rocks of England (Yorkshire excepted)." *Mem. Geol. Survey.*

——, 1902, (1) "Note on the Occurrence of Bagshot Beds at Combe Pyne, near Lyme Regis." *Geol. Mag.*, p. 515.

——, 1902, (2) "Notes on a New Railway in course of construction between Axminster and Lyme Regis." *Summary of Progress, Geol. Survey,* for 1901, p. 53.

——, 1906, "Excursion to Lyme Regis." *Proc. Geol. Assoc.*, vol. XIX., p. 320

W[OODWARD], H. B., 1908, "Burning Cliffs." *Geol. Mag.*, p. 561.

WOODWARD, H. B., and USSHER, W. A. E., 1899, "Excursion to Seaton, Sidmouth, Budleigh Salterton and Exeter." *Proc. Geol. Assoc.*, vol. XVI., p. 133.

——, ——, 1906, "The Geology of the Country near Sidmouth and Lyme Regis." *Mem. Geol. Survey* (second edition, 1911).

WRIGHT, T., 1864, "On the White Lias of Dorsetshire." *Geol. Mag.*, p. 290.

YOUNG, G. W., and LANG, W. D., 1915, "Report of an Excursion to Charmouth and Lyme Regis." *Proc. Geol. Assoc.*, vol. XXVI., p. 111.

ADDITIONS TO THE BIBLIOGRAPHY

AITKEN, W. G., and W. S. McKERROW, 1948. " Rhynchonellids of the Boueti Bed, a Study in Variation." *Geol. Mag.*, p. 19.

ARBER, M. A., 1940, " The Coastal Landslips of South-East Devon." *Proc. Geol. Assoc.*, vol. LI., p. 257.

——, 1941, " The Coastal Landslips of West Dorset." *Proc. Geol. Assoc.*, vol. LII., p. 273.

——1943, " The Microzoa Beds of the Inferior Oolite of Dorset." *Proc. Geol. Assoc.*, vol. LIV., p.113.

——, 1946, " The Valley System of Lyme Regis." *Proc. Geol. Assoc.*, vol. LVII., p. 8.

ARKELL, W. J., 1936, " The Corallian Beds of Dorset. Part I. The Coast." *Proc. Dorset Nat. Hist. and Arch. Soc.*, vol. LVII., p. 59.

——, 1936, " The Tectonics of the Purbeck and Ridgeway Faults in Dorset." *Geol. Mag.*, pp. 56, 97.

——, 1937, Ditto. *Geol. Mag.*, p. 86.

——, 1938, " Three Tectonic Problems of the Lulworth District : Studies on the Middle Limb of the Purbeck Fold." *Quart. Journ. Geol. Soc.*, vol. XCIV., p. 1.

——, 1939, " U-Shaped Burrows in the Corallian Beds of Dorset." *Geol. Mag.*, p. 455.

——, 1941, " The Gastropods of the Purbeck Beds." *Quart. Journ. Geol. Soc.*, vol. XCVII., p. 79.

——, 1945, " The Names of the Strata in the Purbeck and Portland Stone Quarries." *Proc. Dorset Nat. Hist. & Arch. Soc.*, vol. LXVI., p. 158.

——, 1947, " Geology of the Country around Weymouth, Swanage, Corfe and Lulworth." *Mem. Geol. Survey*.

——, 1948, " Oxford Clay and Kellaways Beds., Weymouth." *Proc. Dorset Nat. Hist. & Arch. Soc.*, vol. LXIX., p. 122.

——, 1949, " The Kimeridge Clay Succession at Burning Cliff, Ringstead." *Proc. Dorset Nat. Hist. & Arch. Soc.*, vol. LXX., p. 124.

——, 1949 " Upper Greensand and Lower Chalk in Ringstead Chalk Pit, and a Section through a Positive Lynchet." *Proc. Dorset Nat. Hist. & Arch. Soc.*, vol. LXX., p. 124.

——, 1949, " Erratics in Dorset Shingle Beaches." *Proc. Dorset Nat. Hist. & Arch. Soc.*, vol. LXX., p. 125.

——, 1951, " The Structure of Spring Bottom Ridge, and the Origin of the Mud-slides, Osmington." *Proc. Geol. Assoc.*, vol. LXII., p. 21.

BARNARD, T., 1953, " Foraminifera from the Upper Oxford Clay of Redcliff Point, near Weymouth." *Proc. Geol. Assoc.*, vol. LXIV. p. 183.

——, and J. G. CAPEWELL, 1950, " Field Meeting at Lyme Regis." *Proc. Geol. Assoc.*, vol. LXI., p. 156.

BENFIELD, E., 1940, " Purbeck Shop : a Stoneworker's Story of Stone." Cambridge.

BOMFORD, G., 1948, " New Sections in the Inferior Oolite." *Proc. Geol. Assoc.*, vol. LIX., p. 148.

BOND, W. R. G., 1941, " A Specialised Mesolithic Flint Implement from Blashenwell." *Proc. Dorset Nat. Hist. & Arch. Soc.*, vol. LXII., p. 37.

BURTON, H. ST. J., 1937, " The Origin of Lulworth Cove." *Geol. Mag.*, p. 377.

BURY, H., 1936, " Some Anomalous River-Features in the Isle of Purbeck." *Proc. Geol. Assoc.*, vol. LXVII., p. 1.

——, 1950, " Blashenwell Tufa." *Proc. Bournemouth Nat. Sci. Soc.*, vol. XXXIX., p. 48.

CARRECK, J. N., 1955, " The Quaternary Deposits of Bowleaze Cove, near Weymouth, Dorset." *Proc. Geol. Assoc.*, vol. LXVI., p. 74.

CHATWIN, C. P., 1948, " The Hampshire Basin and Adjoining Areas." Second Edition. *Mem. Geol. Survey.*

CLARK, J. G. D., and A. S. KENNARD, 1938, " Microlithic Industries from Tufa Deposits at Prestatyn, Flintshire, and Blashenwell, Dorset." *Proc. Prehistoric Soc.*, vol. IV. (New Series) p. 330.

FALCON, N. C., and P. E. KENT, 1950, " Chalk Rock of Dorset—more Evidence of Salt ? " *Geol. Mag.*, p. 302.

GREEN, J. F. N., 1947, " Some Gravels and Gravel-pits in Hampshire and Dorset." *Proc. Geol. Assoc.*, vol. LVIII., p. 128.

HOLLINGWORTH, S. E., 1938, " The Purbeck Broken Beds." *Geol. Mag.* p. 330.

KELLAWAY, G. A., and V. WILSON, 1941, " An Outline of the Geology of Yeovil, Sherborne and Sparkford Vale." *Proc. Geol. Assoc.*, vol. LII., p. 131.

KENT, P. E., 1936, " The Formation of the Hydraulic Limestones of the Lower Lias." *Geol. Mag.*, p. 476.

LANG, W. D., 1936, " The Green Ammonite Beds of the Dorset Lias." *Quart. Journ. Geol. Soc.*, vol. XCII., p. 423.

——, 1947, " A Section in the Purbeck and Portland Beds at Perryfield, Portland." *Proc. Dorset Nat. Hist. & Arch. Soc.*, vol. LXVIII., p. 119.

——, 1949, " Cow-Stone." *Proc. Dorset Nat. Hist. & Arch. Soc.*, vol. LXX., p. 147.

——, 1950, " The Post-Eocene Development of the Valley of the Char." *Proc. Geol. Assoc.*, vol. LXI., p. 158.

MOTTRAM, B. H., 1950, " Notes on the Structure of the Poxwell Pericline, and the Ridgeway Fault at Bincombe Tunnel." *Proc. Dorset Nat. Hist. & Arch. Soc.*, vol. LXXI., p. 175.

STEERS, J. A., 1946, " The Coastline of England and Wales." Cambridge.

SYLVESTER-BRADLEY, P. C., 1948, " Field Meeting at Weymouth." *Proc. Geol. Assoc.*, vol. LIX., p. 141.

——, 1949, " A Section of the Purbeck Beds at Poxwell." *Proc. Geol. Assoc.*, vol. LX., p. 151.

TAITT, A. H., and P. E. KENT, 1939, " Notes on an Examination of the Poxwell Anticline, Dorset." *Geol. Mag.*, p. 173.

INDEX

This book is to be ed on befo
he be